SCOTTISH
QUIZ
BOOK

SCOTTISH

QUIZ

BOOK

LOMOND BOOKS

First published in 1999 by Lomond Books
36 West Shore Road, Granton,
Edinburgh EH5 1QD

24681097531

Copyright © Miles Kelly Publishing Ltd
1999

ISBN 0 947782 29 X

Questions composed and edited by Sean Connolly

Project Manager: Ian Paulyn
Editor: Kate Miles
Designer: Jo Brewer

Cover tartan, Royal Stewart, supplied by
Peter MacArthur & Co Ltd, Hamilton, Scotland

In ploughman phrase, 'God send you speed,'
Still daily to grow wiser,
And may ye better reck the rede,
Than ever did th'adviser!

from 'Epistle to a Young Friend',
by Robert Burns

With the Scottish Parliament ready to usher in the new Millennium, what better time is there to test your knowledge about all things Caledonian? The *Scottish Quiz Book* provides the chance to do just that. Inside you will find more than 4000 questions spread across a wide range of Scottish interest. The topics covered are People, Places, History, Sport, TV and Entertainment, Music and Literature, General Knowledge and Trivia. There's a chance to shine, whether your speciality is Jedburgh Abbey, Jekyll and Hyde, or Jocky Wilson. And for those who have shown that they are no 'dunces' (see Trivia, quiz 2), there is the chance to pit their brains against the Great Scot competition – 80 questions designed to find the 'creme de la creme' (to borrow a phrase from the Auld Alliance) among those taking part.

CONTENTS

TV & ENTERTAINMENT

1 Who directed the film *Gregory's Girl?*

2 In which year was television first broadcast in Scotland?

3 In which television series would you follow the course of events in Lochdubh?

4 Which film-maker, often called the Father of the Documentary, directed the classic *Night Mail?*

5 Which Scottish Olympic gold medal-winner was portrayed in the film *Chariots of Fire?*

6 Who played Gregory's girl in *Gregory's Girl?*

7 Who was the lead singer of Altered Images?

8 Which singer was born Marie MacDonald McLaughlin Lawrie in 1948?

9 Which folk-singer wrote Elvis Presley's Grammy award-winning 'The First Time Ever I Saw Your Face'?

10 Which Glasgow-born musician formed Pentangle in 1967 with John Renbourn?

11 Where was Annie Lennox born?

12 What was the name of the 1980s Glasgow record label that launched Orange Juice and Aztec Camera?

13 Who was the falsetto-voiced lead singer of Bronski Beat and the Communards?

14 Who succeeded Sir Robin Day as presenter of *The World At One?*

15 Who played Eric Liddell in *Chariots of Fire?*

ANSWERS

1. Bill Forsyth 2. 1926 3. *Hamish Macbeth* 4. John Grierson 5. Eric Liddell 6. Dee Hepburn 7. Clare Grogan 8. Lulu 9. Ewan MacColl 10. Bert Jansch 11. Aberdeen 12. Postcard 13. Jimmy Somerville 14. James Naughtie 15. Ian Charleson

SPORT

1 Which golf course hosted the first Open Championships in 1867?

2 How many Formula One World Driver's Championships did Jackie Stewart win?

3 Love Street is the home of which Scottish football club?

4 Where is the Mosstroopers Race Meeting held each July?

5 Which variation of a major sport was first played in Melrose?

6 Which king decreed that soldiers not play golf?

7 Falkland Palace, west of St Andrews, contains Britain's oldest venue for which sport?

8 Which Irish sport is the nearest relative to shinty?

9 Where did the first Highland Games take place?

10 Who is the Royal Patron of the Scottish Rugby Union?

11 Graham Obree is a top performer in which sport?

12 In which year did Sandy Lyle win the Masters in Augusta, Georgia?

13 What is a 'hack' in curling?

14 Where would you need to go to attend the Ba' Games?

15 When did Sir Matt Busby become manager of Manchester United?

ANSWERS

1. Prestwick Old Golf Course 2. Three 3. St Mirren 4. Hawick 5. Seven-a-side rugby 6. James I 7. (Real) tennis 8. Hurling 9. Braemar 10. Princess Anne 11. Pursuit cycling 12. 1988 13. A foothold 14. Kirkwall 15. 1945

PEOPLE

1 In 1953 Sean Connery represented Scotland in which competition, coming third?

2 Whose by-election victory in 1967 sparked the rebirth of the SNP?

3 In which year was William Wallace betrayed to the English and executed?

4 Which king created the 'Royal Burghs'?

5 Who was Scotland's last Lord Privy Seal?

6 Which king extended Scottish dominion south to the Tweed in 1018?

7 Who was responsible for the Arbroath Declaration in 1320?

8 Who used the upland setting of the Cairnsmore of Fleet as a major setting in a famous spy novel?

9 Which 13th-century vassal king was known to his subjects as Toom Tabard (Empty Coat)?

10 Who compiled a list of all Scottish peaks over 3000 feet in 1891?

11 What was the Queen Mother's full name when she married the future George VI?

12 Which clan was known as the 'Nameless Clan'?

13 Which monarch was the first to change the spelling of Stewart to Stuart to denote royal blood?

14 Who was the architect of Charlotte Square, Edinburgh and Culzean Castle?

15 Andrew is the patron saint of Scotland and which other European country?

ANSWERS

1. Mister Universe 2. Winifred Ewing 3. 1305 4. David I 5. The Earl of Seafield 6. Malcolm II 7. Robert the Bruce 8. John Buchan: *The 39 Steps* 9. John Baliol 10. Sir Hugh Munro 11. Lady Elizabeth Bowes-Lyon 12. The MacGregors, who were outlawed from 1603 to 1774 13. Mary, Queen of Scots 14. Robert Adam 15. Russia

MUSIC & LITERATURE

1   In the ballad 'Edward', what was Edward's crime?

2   Which of Shakespeare's plays is known as 'the Scottish play'?

3   In the Scottish story 'The Frog Prince', where does the heroine meet the frog?

4   In 'The Black Bull of Norway' the heroine is helped by an apple, a pear and what other type of fruit?

5   What was the name of Sir Walter Scott's last, and most famous, house?

6   Who created the fictional 'Rathan Isle' in his novel *The Raiders*?

7   Which subject of an enduring love song lived in Maxwellton House, near Thornhill?

8   Deacon Brodie, an 18th-century Edinburgh town councillor who was executed for burglary, was the inspiration for which famous novel?

9   What was Sir Walter Scott's first novel?

10 Who wrote the novel *Trainspotting*?

11 On which Pacific island did Robert Louis Stevenson spend his last years, for health reasons?

12 Which loch forms the setting for Scott's *The Lady of the Lake*?

13 Which 18th-century Gaelic poet is referred to as the 'Burns of the Highlands'?

14 The basalt columns on the Hebridean island of Staffa inspired a major piece by which German composer?

15 The SS *Politicia*, carrying 20,000 cases of whisky, sank in 1941, inspiring Compton Mackenzie to write *Whisky Galore*. On which island did it wreck?

ANSWERS

1. He killed his father 2. *Macbeth* 3. At the well 4. A plum 5. Abbotsford House
6. S R Crockett 7. Annie Laurie 8. *Doctor Jekyll and Mr Hyde* 9. *Waverley*: 1814 10. Irvine
Welsh 11. Samoa 12. Loch Katrine 13. Duncan Ban McIntyre 14. Mendelssohn 15. Eriskay

GENERAL KNOWLEDGE

1   What is the dish Powsodie made with?

2   Cashmere is a thriving industry in Scotland, but where does the fibre come from?

3   What were Marchmen?

4   What is a 'gare'?

5   What is another name for the reivers, or Borders bandits?

6   What are Jethart snails?

7   Near which Annandale town would you find the Devil's Beef Tub?

8   Baldoon Castle, in the extreme west of Dumfries and Galloway, was the setting for which Sir Walter Scott novel?

9   Which famous scientist was born in Loudon, Galston, in 1881?

10 James Watt, inventor of the steam engine, was born in which Clyde ship-building town?

11 What type of hill is described as a 'dod'?

12 Lorraine soup is named after whom?

13 William and Robert Chambers, publishers of dictionaries and encyclopedias, founded the Chambers Institute in which town?

14 What did the 'Four Marys', famous in the 16th century, have in common?

15 Some 129 men, almost all of the male population of which fishing town, died in a storm in in October 1881?

ANSWERS

1. A sheep's head 2. Goats on the plains of Mongolia – it is a downy undercoat 3. Men of the border 4. A skirt 5. Mosstroopers 6. hard toffees 7. Moffat 8. *The Bride of Lammermoor* 9. Sir Alexander Fleming 10. Greenock 11. One with a rounded summit 12. Mary of Lorraine, wife of James V 13. Peebles 14. They were ladies-in-waiting to Mary, Queen of Scots 15. Eyemouth

PLACES

1   Where is the centre of Scotland's cashmere industry?

2   Name the bird sanctuary that lies off the coast of Troon.

3   What is the highest peak in the Scottish Lowlands?

4   Which town was the birthplace of James I in 1394?

5   'Sour Plums' is the motto of which town?

6   Which town did Sir Walter Scott describe as 'the most beautiful, if not the most romantic, village in Scotland'?

7   Where was James VI (James I of England) crowned?

8   The desolate region known as the Glenkins lies north of which forth?

9   Princes Street, Edinburgh, is named after which monarch's sons?

10 In which town would you find the Jim Clark Museum?

11 Which two rivers rise within a mile of each other in the Southern Uplands?

12 In 1922, the record for the largest salmon caught by rod was set on which Scottish river?

13 How high is Ben Nevis?

14 Which famous historian, essayist and critic was born in Lockerbie in 1795?

15 How many Scottish islands are there: a) 617, b) 731, c) 787

ANSWERS

1. Hawick 2. Lady Isle 3. Merrick: 844 m/2770 ft 4. Dunfermline 5. Galashiels 6. Kelso 7. Stirling Castle 8. Solway 9. George III 10. Duns 11. Clyde and Tweed 12. Tay 13. 1343 m/4406 ft 14. Thomas Carlyle 15. c) 787

HISTORY

1 What was the name of the kingdom established by Irish invaders in the sixth century?

2 Who was crowned as the first king of a united Scotland in 844?

3 In which year was the first North Sea oil flow ashore?

4 Where was Robert the Bruce's heart laid to rest?

5 Which king died in Flodden Field in 1513?

6 In which year were the Coldstream Guards raised?

7 Bonnie Prince Charlie's troops took only ten minutes to capture Sir John Cope's army outside which town in 1745?

8 What was the 'Rough Wooing' of 1545?

9 How many times has Berwick changed hands between Scotland and England?

10 Who landed on Iona in AD563 to missionize Scotland?

11 Which king was the father of Mary, Queen of Scots?

12 In which year was the Stone of Scone stolen from Scotland by Edward I of England?

13 In which year was the Stone of Scone returned to Scotland?

14 What was the name of the Greek monk who, according to legend, founded St Andrews?

15 In which year did the Glencoe Massacre take place?

ANSWERS

1. Dalriada 2. Kenneth MacAlpine 3. 1975 4. Melrose Abbey 5. James IV 6. 1650
7. Prestonpans 8. Henry VIII tried to bully the Scots into a marriage between his son Edward and the infant Mary, Queen of Scots 9. Thirteen 10. Saint Columba 11. James V
12. 1297 13. 1996 14. Regulus (or Rule) 15. 1692

TRIVIA

1   What was a 'reiver'?

2   Which firth was the western end of Hadrian's Wall?

3   Which is the only Scottish football club located in England?

4   The first Coldstream Guards served in whose army?

5   How long was the old Scots measurement known as an ell?

6   What sort of natural feature is Grey Mare's Tail?

7   Which remarkable 16th-century native of Sanquhar, near Moffat, was fluent in 12 languages, known as 'the Marvel of Europe' and became immortalized in a play by J. M. Barrie?

8   The Brig o'Doon, mentioned in Burns's poem 'Tam o' Shanter', spans the river in which town?

9   Which 19th-century Kilmarnock grocer began to blend whisky and established what is now the world's largest spirits bottling company?

10 What is the Electric Brae, 5 miles north of the west coast town of Maybole?

11 What appears on the coat of arms of Peebles, above a Latin motto reading 'Against the stream they multiply'?

12 Within ten feet, how high above the Firth of Forth is the Forth Bridge?

13 What was unusual about Gladstone's Midlothian Campaign of 1879?

14 Spell out Bo'ness in full.

15 Part of Castle Esplanade in Edinburgh is marked as belonging to which overseas province?

ANSWERS

1. A Borders cattle rustler 2. Solway 3. Berwick Rangers 4. Cromwell's New Model Army 5. 37 inches/94 cm 6. A waterfall 7. James Crichton 8. Ayr 9. Johnny Walker 10. An optical illusion: the road seems to be descending when it is actually climbing 11. Three salmon 12. 512 ft/156 m 13. It was the first whistle-stop campaign by a British Party leader 14. Barrowstounness 15. Nova Scotia

TV & ENTERTAINMENT

1 Which performer is nicknamed 'the Big Yin'?

2 Which actor played the title role in the television series *Taggart*?

3 *Tight Little Island* was the American title for which famous Scottish film?

4 What was the name of the film starring Judi Dench as Queen Victoria and Billy Connolly as her attendant?

5 Who played Mrs Proudie in the BBC adaptation of Trollope's *Barchester Towers*?

6 Who played Mr Hudson in *Upstairs, Downstairs,* and the boss of CI5 in *The Professionals?*

7 Which band had hits with 'Broken Down Angel' and 'Bad Bad Boy' in the 1970s?

8 What was Deacon Blue's first top ten hit?

9 What instrument did Ian Anderson of Jethro Tull play?

10 Which comedian, born in Edinburgh in 1930, has the middle name Balfour?

11 Charlie and Craig Reid are better known as what?

12 Where do The Proclaimers come from?

13 Who plays Rab C Nesbitt?

14 Who plays Rab's wife?

15 Which band's drummer, Robbie McIntosh, died of a heroin overdose in 1974?

ANSWERS

1. Billy Connolly 2. Mark McManus 3. *Whisky Galore* 4. *Mrs Brown* 5. Geraldine McEwan 6. Gordon Jackson 7. Nazareth 8. *Real Gone Kid* 9. Flute 10. Ronnie Corbett 11. The Proclaimers 12. Auchtermuchtie 13. Gregor Fisher 14. Elaine C. Smith 15. Average White Band

SPORT

1   Former racing driver Johnny Dumfries has a title. What is it?

2   Who was the first Scot to hold a world boxing title in 1935?

3   How much does a curling stone weigh?

4   How many players are there on a shinty team?

5   How many Grand Prix wins did Jim Clark amass in his career?

6   With which sport was businessman and philanthropist Sir Thomas Lipton associated?

7   Dundee United only became 'United' in 1923. Under what name were they founded in 1909?

8   Where was Liz McColgan born?

9   Scotland have had six world boxing champions, three each at 2 weights – which ones?

10 Who was Scotland's manager for the 1974 World Cup finals?

11 When did Stephen Hendry win his first World Snooker championship, becoming the youngest player ever to do so?

12 Who captained both Scotland and the British Lions in 1989?

13 At which Olympics did David Wilkie win his gold medal in the 200 metre breaststroke?

14 Whom did Scotland beat at Hampden in September 1973 (in front of 100,000 people) to qualify for the finals?

15 Against whom did Scotland score their only point, in a 0-0 draw, in the 1986 World Cup finals in Mexico?

ANSWERS

1. Marquis of Bute 2. Benny Lynch 3. 20 kg/44 lb 4. Twelve 5. Twenty-five 6. Yacht racing 7. Dundee Hibernians 8. Dundee 9. Flyweight and lightweight 10. Willie Ormond 11. 1990 12. Finlay Calder 13. 1976 in Montreal 14. Czechoslovakia 15. Uruguay

PEOPLE

1 Which clan has the oldest documented tartan?

2 With which field of science would you associate Robert Adamson?

3 Which king succeeded William I in 1214?

4 The engineer Sir William Arrol designed the Forth railway bridge and which bridge in London?

5 Which Scottish scientist was the pioneer of television?

6 With which agricultural invention would you associate Patrick Bell?

7 Which type of colourful children's toy was invented by Sir David Brewster?

8 Which Scottish explorer discovered the source of the Blue Nile?

9 Burke and Hare were infamous in Edinburgh for what type of activity?

10 James Chalmers invented what type of aid to communications?

11 Who was the second husband of Mary, Queen of Scots?

12 Sir Arthur Conan Doyle shared a professional training with which of his famous characters?

13 The soldier Patrick Ferguson invented what type of weapon?

14 What cabinet office was Iain Macleod holding at the time of his death in 1970?

15 Who was the steel industrialist born in Dunfermline in 1835 who became a multimillionaire in the USA and retired in 1901 to Skibo Castle in Sutherland, giving millions of dollars to public institutions?

ANSWERS

1. MacLean 2.Chemistry 3. Alexander II 4. Tower Bridge 5. John Logie Baird 6. The mechanical reaper 7. Kaleidoscope 8. James Bruce 9. Body-snatching 10. Adhesive postage stamps 11. Lord Darnley 12. Doctor Watson 13. Breech-loading rifle 14. Chancellor of the Exchequer 15. Andrew Carnegie

MUSIC & LITERATURE

1 Which composer set the ballad 'Sir Patrick Spens' to music?

2 In the story 'Tam Lin', how does Janet win him back from the fairies?

3 What does the word 'drie' mean?

4 Which poet was known as 'the Ettrick Shepherd'?

5 Which tower was the setting of Sir Walter Scott's ballad 'The Eve of St John'?

6 Who wrote *Ring of Bright Water?*

7 Who was the most famous member of the Bachelors Club in Tarbolton?

8 Which famous pair set off from Auchinleck House in 1773 for a tour of the Hebrides?

9 In which town would you find the permanent memorial to the playwright J M Barrie?

10 Who wrote the novel *St Ives?*

11 Who gained notoriety for his bad verse in the 19th century?

12 Which town is known as 'Thrums' in the novels of J M Barrie?

13 Which poet and clergyman is sometimes called 'the father of Scottish poetry and history'?

14 With which art form would you associate Dame Isobel Baillie?

15 Which convicted murderer later became widely acclaimed as a writer and sculptor?

ANSWERS

1. Robert Pearsall 2. She holds him in her arms until he turns into a man and the fairies concede defeat 3. Suffer 4. James Hogg 5. Smailholm Tower 6. Gavin Maxwell 7. Robert Burns 8. James Boswell and Dr Samuel Johnson 9. Kirriemuir 10. Robert Louis Stevenson 11. William McGonagall 12. Kirriemuir 13. John Barbour 14. Opera 15. Jimmy Boyle

GENERAL KNOWLEDGE

1. What does 'couth' mean?

2. What is Pantan Pie made from?

3. What type of hill is descibed as a 'law'?

4. What did Edinburgh residents formerly shout when dumping chamberpots from upper-storey windows?

5. Which Scottish chemist discovered carbon dioxide?

6. Where was the political economist Adam Smith born?

7. In which year was the first Edinburgh Festival held?

8. Which Glasgow native founded the world's largest private investigating organization in the United States?

9. What is Provand's Lordship?

10. How many Munros (mountains over 3000 feet) were cited in the first list in 1891?

11. Marischal College, Aberdeen, is the second largest granite building in the world; what is the largest?

12. What is Ogham script?

13. What is the name of the huge cannon on display in Edinburgh Castle?

14. What does the 'rood' of Holyrood Palace mean?

15. Which warrior clan had the battle cry 'Sons of dogs, come here and get flesh'?

ANSWERS

1. Word 2. Crab 3. A conical hill 4. 'Gardyloo' 5. Joseph Black 6. Kirkcaldy 7. 1947 8. Allan Pinkerton 9. The oldest building in Glasgow 10. 277 11. El Escorial, near Madrid 12. A type of carved lettering using lines and cross-hatching 13. Mons Meg 14. Cross 15. Cameron

2

1   Charles I (of England) was born in which Scottish town?

2   On which island is former Labour Party leader John Smith buried?

3   Which cathedral, now in ruins, was once Britain's largest church?

4   What is the largest island in Orkney?

5   In which town is Robert Burns buried?

6   The Hillsfoot Towns, a major textile-producing area, lie northeast of which town?

7   Ben Ledi is the highest of which group of hills?

8   What is Britain's most northerly city?

9   The ruins of which castle overlook Loch Ness?

10 Which range of hills dominates the landscape of Skye?

11 Dunadd Fort, on the Mull of Kintyre, was the capital of which ancient kingdom?

12 Which road, known as the 'Road to the Isles', connects Fort William with Mallaig?

13 What does 'voe' mean in place names in Shetland?

14 Which castle was long known as Castle Gloom?

15 In which castle was Princess Margaret born?

ANSWERS

1. Dunfermline 2. Iona 3. St Andrews 4. Mainland of Orkney 5. Dumfries 6. Stirling 7. The Trossachs 8. Aberdeen 9. Urquhart 10. The Cuillins 11. Dalriada 12. The A830 13. Long sea-channel 14. Castle Campbell, near Dollar 15. Glamis

HISTORY

1 Where did Bonnie Prince Charlie first land on Scottish soil?

2 Which Scottish Royalist general, executed by Cromwell, had his limbs and head displayed around the country?

3 Which architect won the 1767 competition to design a new district for Edinburgh?

4 Which general, having learned of Charles I's execution, swore that he would never cut his hair or shave until the monarchy was restored?

5 In which year was the Poll Tax introduced in Scotland?

6 Which famous Scottish regiment was raised in 1729?

7 In which year was Hadrian's Wall begun?

8 What was the name of the warship launched at Newhaven in 1511, its 210-foot/64 m length making it the largest ship to date?

9 What was the price put on the Young Pretender's head in the aftermath of the Battle of Culloden?

10 Which king founded Aberdeen University?

11 Which monarch visited Edinburgh in 1822?

12 How is Saint Kentigern better known?

13 *Comet,* the first European steam boat, was built by which Scottish engineer?

14 The first Prime Minister of Canada was born in Glasgow. Name him.

15 Lachlan Macquarrie, a colonial administrator, was known as 'the father' of which country?

ANSWERS

1. Eriskay 2. The Marquis of Montrose 3. James Craig 4. Tam Dalyell 5. 1989 6. The Black Watch 7. AD120 8. *The Great Michael* 9. £30,000 10. James IV 11. George IV 12. As Saint Mungo 13. Henry Bell 14. Sir John Macdonald 15. Australia

24

1 What aspect of George IV's clothing stood out glaringly when he attended a ball in 1822 dressed in full Highlands regalia?

2 What purpose do 'jougs' serve?

3 Where does Norse Udall law apply?

4 What is the name of the cocktail made of three parts whisky to one part cream?

5 A 'babbity buster' can be either of two things; one is a children's game. What is the other?

6 What does the 'sauchie' in Glasgow's Sauchiehall Street mean?

7 Which person and place are commemorated in the word 'dunce'?

8 In which industry would you come across the 'angel's share'?

9 The town of Keith is the birthplace of which newspaperman whose name became an epithet?

10 The stretch of the A832 from Gairloch to Poolewe has what nickname?

11 'Evidence' of what mystery are exhibited at Drumnadrochit?

12 What does the 'Wrath' of Cape Wrath mean in the Norse language?

13 Which mineral causes the bright speckling in the granite of Aberdeen?

14 What is the name of the revolving mirror that reflects an image of Edinburgh against a white surface in the Outlook Tower?

15 'Nosing' is an important function in what sort of job?

ANSWERS

1. Pink silk tights 2. As a collar for chaining criminals to a wall 3. Along the coast of Shetland 4. Noose-loosener 5. A country dance 6. A willow 7. The 13th-century philosopher John Duns Scotus, who was born in Duns 8. Distilling: it is the whisky that evaporates through wooden casks 9. James Gordon Bennett 10. The Destitution Road 11. The Loch Ness Monster 12. Turning-point 13. Mica 14. Camera Obscura 15. Master brewer (sniffing how to blend whiskies)

TV & ENTERTAINMENT

1 In which village is *Take The High Road* set?

2 What is the name of the actress who is Emma Thompson's mother?

3 Which pop singer called her daughter Lola?

4 Who was the lead singer of Ultravox who helped Bob Geldof organise Live Aid?

5 In what make of car did Robbie Coltrane travel across America in his TV series?

6 Who is the lead singer of Wet Wet Wet?

7 Of which band is Sharleen Spiteri the lead singer?

8 Which entertainer said: 'Roses are red, violets are blue, I'm schizophrenic, and so am I'?

9 Which Scottish actor plays Victor Meldrew?

10 For which 1987 film did Sean Connery win an Oscar?

11 Who played William Wallace in *Braveheart?*

12 Who were the stars of the comedy series set in an airline company, *The High Life?*

13 Which Scottish actress, who starred in *The Life and Death of Colonel Blimp* and *Black Narcissus* early in her career, was nominated six times for an Oscar?

14 Which comedian played the part of Daniel Defoe in the BBC adaptation of *Moll Flanders?*

15 Who played Gregory in *Gregory's Girl?*

ANSWERS

SPORT

1   Who won the men's 100 metres at the 1980 Olympics in Moscow?

2   A caber is usually made from the trunk of what type of tree?

3   Which team play at Stair Park?

4   Which southern Scottish town was the birthplace of the Rugby Sevens in 1883?

5   Which team did Billy Bremner manage after he finished his playing career at Leeds United in 1978?

6   Apart from motor-racing, at which other sport did Jackie Stewart excel, reaching near-Olympic standard?

7   In which month is the Glasgow Marathon run?

8   How many stones must be delivered to complete an end in curling?

9   Where is the achery competition known as 'Shooting for the Silver Arrow' held each May?

10 From which Italian club did Matt Busby sign Denis Law for Manchester United in 1962?

11 Who beat Stephen Hendry in the 1998 Embassy World Snooker Championship?

12 Scott Hastings is director of rugby for which team?

13 By the end of 1998 how many world titles had Stephen Hendry amassed?

14 What was the outcome of the 1961 cup-tie between Manchester City and Luton in which Denis Law scored six goals?

15 In how many of Stephen Hendry's six World Championships between 1990 and 1996 did he beat Jimmy White in the final?

ANSWERS

1. Alan Wells 2. Fir 3. Stranraer 4. Melrose 5. Doncaster Rovers 6. Clay-pigeon shooting 7. September 8. Sixteen 9. Musselburgh Links 10. Torino 11. Ken Doherty 12. Watsonians 13. Six 14. The match was abandoned! 15. 4

PEOPLE

1 Thomas Chalmers was the founder of which religious institution?

2 Which historical figure was born in Edinburgh and went on to become Commander of the Irish Army during the Easter Uprising of 1916?

3 Which clan chief lives in Dunvegan Castle in Skye?

4 Which king of Scotland was the son of Robert the Bruce?

5 Why do many people think of Sir James Dewar when they pack a picnic?

6 Robert Ferguson was a well-known conspirator against which two kings?

7 With which mode of transport would you associate Dugald Drummond?

8 The civil engineer Sir Sandford Fleming spanned a continent with which of his major projects?

9 The chemist and physicist Thomas Graham formulated Graham's Law. To what does this law pertain?

10 Who commanded the British Army in the First World War?

11 James Hutton is credited with having founded the modern study of which science?

12 James I was the son of which other Scottish king?

13 Olympic medallist Eric Liddell went on to pursue what type of career?

14 J J R Macleod was the co-discoverer of which medical hormone?

15 In which constituency has Tam Dalyell been MP for many years?

ANSWERS

1. The Free Church of Scotland 2. James Connolly 3. MacLeod 4. David II 5. He invented the vacuum flask 6. Charles II and James II of England 7. Trains; he was a locomotive engineer 8. Completing the Canadian Pacific Railway 9. The diffusion of gases 10. Earl Haig 11. Geology 12. Robert III 13. Christian missionary 14. Insulin 15. West Lothian

MUSIC & LITERATURE

1 A famous Scottish ballad about patricide provided the inspiration for which German composer?

2 In 'Lord Thomas' Fair Annett', the graves of the tragic lovers have what type of plants on them?

3 Robert Paterson, an eccentric wandering stonemason, was the inspiration for which Sir Walter Scott novel?

4 The writer John Buchan became Governor-General of which Commonwealth country?

5 Which profession links William Blackwood and William Collins?

6 With which form of writing would you associate Gavin Douglas?

7 Who wrote the novel *Sunset Song*?

8 With which art form would you associate Sir Alexander Gibson?

9 Songwriter Niel Gow is known for playing which musical instrument?

10 Who wrote *Ice Station Zebra?*

11 Who was the real-life castaway who inspired Daniel Defoe to write *Robinson Crusoe?*

12 The editor and printer William Smellie published the first edition of which famous title?

13 Who wrote *The Adventures of Roderick Random?*

14 With which two artistic endeavours would you associate Ian Hamilton Finlay?

15 The 18th-century poet James H D Thomson wrote which famous patriotic verses?

ANSWERS

1. Brahms 2. A birch tree and a briar 3. Old Mortality 4. Canada 5. publishing 6. poetry 7. Lewis Grassic Gibbon 8. Music (orchestral conductor) 9. Violin 10. Alistair McLean 11. Alexander Selkirk 12. Encyclopaedia Britannica 13. Tobias Smollett 14. Poetry and painting 15. 'Rule Britannia'

3

1   The name of which large bird, native to the Highlands, translates as 'horse of the woods'?

2   How many letters are there in the Gaelic alphabet?

3   In which American city did Scottish inventor Alexander Graham Bell first demonstrate the telephone?

4   What type of hill is described as a 'rig'?

5   Which American president is commemorated with a statue on Edinburgh's Calton Hill?

6   In which year was Glasgow named the Cultural Capital of Europe?

7   What is Howtowdie?

8   Culzean Castle contains a special National Guest Flat; who was the honoured foreign guest?

9   What does 'Aber' mean in a place name?

10 Which clan cherishes a Fairy Flag, said to make them invincible in battle?

11 What was the first book to be published in Gaelic?

12 Blair Castle is the home of which titled aristocrats?

13 In which city's shipyards were the polar exploration ships of both Scott and Shackleton built?

14 Which native of Stonehaven invented the pneumatic tyre, the fountain pen and the dry dock?

15 Which type of bird returned to nest in Boat of Garten in 1958, after the species had been wiped out on British soil 48 years earlier?

ANSWERS

1. Capercaillie 2. 18 3. Boston 4. A ridge 5. Abraham Lincoln 6. 1990 7. A chicken stew with poached eggs 8. General (and later President) Dwight Eisenhower 9. River mouth 10. MacLeod 11. Bishop John Carswell's translation of John Knox's Liturgy 12. Dukes of Atholl 13. Dundee 14. Robert William Thomson 15. Osprey

30

PLACES

1 Which is the most northerly Shetland Island?

2 In which palace was Rizzio, secretary to Mary, Queen of Scots, murdered?

3 Where would you find Argyll's Ludging?

4 Who was the most famous prisoner held at Lochleven Castle, located on an island in the loch of the same name?

5 How long did Hadrian's Wall run: a) 61 miles b) 119 miles c) 73 miles?

6 What tragedy is associated with the Prentice Pillar at Roslin Chapel?

7 What forms the western end of Edinburgh's Royal Mile?

8 Which place is often called the 'Lang Toun'?

9 Which glen is known as the Glen of Weeping?

10 The motto of which city is 'Bon Accord'?

11 What are the 'parallel roads' of Glen Roy?

12 Where would you go to witness the Up-Helly-Ha festival?

13 The name of which Hebridean island means 'island of the cloud' in Norse?

14 What is the second highest mountain in Scotland?

15 What is the name of Aberdeen's airport?

ANSWERS

1. Muckle Flugga 2. Holyroodhouse 3. Stirling 4. Mary, Queen of Scots 5. c: 73 miles/117 Km 6. It was carved by an apprentice, whose jealous master killed him when he returned from a journey 7. Castle Hill 8. Kirkcaldy 9. Glencoe 10. Aberdeen 11. Former shorelines of lakes formed during the Ice Ages 12. Lerwick 13. Skye 14. Ben MacDhui 15. Dyce

1 In which year did Queen Victoria first visit Scotland?

2 Which famous engineering project was completed in 1890?

3 Which famous Act relating to rural land-owning came into effect in 1886?

4 What element of Scottish culture was banned in 1746?

5 Which important religious document was signed in 1557?

6 Why did Alexander I found an abbey at Aberdour in 1123?

7 From where was James VI kidnapped in 1582 by angry Protestant noblemen?

8 When was the first Tay Railway Bridge opened?

9 In which year was the Skye Bridge completed?

10 Princess Louise of Stolberg was married to which historical figure?

11 James Stuart, the Regent of Scotland and half-brother of Mary, Queen of Scots, was whose illegitimate son?

12 The clergyman and writer John Witherspoon signed which famous historical document?

13 Which English king did Robert the Bruce defeat at Bannockburn?

14 What was the name of the petition to the Pope in which the Scots, under Robert the Bruce, asserted their right to independence in 1320?

15 In which year did Macbeth murder Duncan?

ANSWERS

1. 1842 2. The Forth Bridge 3. The Crofters Act 4. Highland dress 5. The First Covenant 6. To give thanks for being saved from a shipwreck 7. Huntingtower Castle 8. 1878 9. 1995 10. Bonnie Prince Charlie 11. James V 12. The American Declaration of Independence 13. Edward II 14. The Arbroath Declaration 15. 1040

3

1 What does 'cath-dath' mean in relation to tartans?

2 McCaig's Tower, in Oban, is an unfinished replica of which famous building?

3 What was the real name of Rob Roy?

4 What is the 'Forfar Bridle'?

5 What is a 'howe'?

6 'Big Peter', a 300-year-old bell, sounds a ten o'clock curfew in which town?

7 'Balmoral' is a corruption of the Gaelic word 'Bouchmorale', meaning what?

8 Which is Scotland's oldest working malt-whisky distillery?

9 How many locks are there on the Caledoninan Canal?

10 The first Cabinet meeting to be held outside London took place in 1921 – in which town?

11 What is an 'Each Uisge'?

12 What was noteworthy about the French brig (Du Teillay)?

13 How tall (in hands or inches) is a Shetland pony when fully grown?

14 Who is the patron saint of Glasgow?

15 Which famous pirate, hanged in 1701, was born in Greenock?

ANSWERS

1. War-colour 2. The Colosseum in Rome 3. Robert MacGregor 4. A medieval iron collar with a prong to gag condemned prisoners 5. A hollow or sheltered place 6. Montrose 7. Majestic dwelling 8. Strath Isla: 1785 9. 29 10. Inverness 11. One of the legendary water-horses said to live in Highland lochs 12. It brought Bonnie Prince Charlie to Scotland 13. 13 hands (42 inches) 14. Saint Kentigern, or Mungo 15. William Kidd, or 'Captain Kidd'.

TV & ENTERTAINMENT

1 Which international screen star had early roles in *Go Now, Carla's Song* and *Face?*

2 Which television series is filmed in the village of Plockton?

3 Which Glasgow-based band were known as Dean Ford and the Gaylords during the first half of the 60s, before moving to London and changing their name?

4 What was the name of the character played by Frazer Hines in *Dr Who?*

5 Who is Jimmy Logan's famous sister?

6 Born Derek William Dick in Dalkeith, Edinburgh in 1958, he is the lead singer of a band whose biggest selling album was *Misplaced Childhood* in 1985. What is he better known as?

7 Who had a hit in 1984 with *Fields of Fire (400 Miles)?*

8 Who played Janet in *Dr Finlay's Casebook?*

9 Who directed the film *Local Hero?*

10 Including Alex Harvey, how many members were there in the Sensational Alex Harvey Band?

11 Who played Mr Mackay in *Porridge?*

12 Which TV presenter wrote a book on the Munros?

13 Which Scottish band had hits with 'Soley Soley' and 'Chirpy Chirpy Cheep Cheep'?

14 Which actress played Tattie Mackintosh in *ITMA,* and was in a long-running advert for Flash?

15 What is Donovan's surname?

ANSWERS

1. Robert Carlyle 2. *Hamish Macbeth* 3. Marmalade 4. Jamie 5. Annie Ross 6. Fish (of Marillion) 7. Big Country 8. Barbara Mullen 9. Bill Forsyth 10. Five 11. Fulton Mackay 12. Muriel Gray 13. Middle of the Road 14. Molly Weir 15. Leitch

SPORT

1 Which two Scots were in the winning Ryder Cup team in 1985?

2 In which sport do the Scottish Claymores play?

3 In which sport are scores given in 'hails'?

4 At which club did Jim Baxter begin his career?

5 Whom did John Higgins beat in the 1998 World Snooker Championship Final?

6 Apart from Jackie Stewart, who was Scotland's other World Motor-racing champion?

7 How many World Cup finals did Graeme Souness take part in?

8 How far did Stephen Hendry advance in the 1999 UK Snooker Championships?

9 Which European club did Graeme Souness manage between Liverpool and Southampton?

10 For which top rugby team does Ian MacAusland play?

11 In which sport would you have a 'bonspiel'?

12 How many centuries did John Higgins achieve in the 1998 Embassy World Snooker Championships?

13 Which Hibernian player scored 22 goals in 38 games for Scotland?

14 Which company withdrew its support for the Scottish Rugby Union during the 1998-9 season?

15 What is the name of Queen of the South's ground?

ANSWERS

1. Sandy Lyle and Sam Torrance 2. American football 3. shinty 4. Raith Rovers 5. Ken Doherty 6. Jim Clark 7. 3 – 1978, 1982 and 1986 8. Lost in the first round 9. Galatasaray 10. London Scottish 11. Curling 12. Six 13. Lawrie Reilly 14. Tennents 15. Palmerston Park

PEOPLE

1   Who founded the Scottish Labour Party?

2   The medical reformer Elsie Maud Inglis was a prominent supporter of what other cause?

3   Scottish doctor James Lind was the first to use citrus fruits to cure which disease?

4   Which politician said: 'The reason they think I'm bonkers is because I have original views and speak my mind'?

5   Which Scottish inventor was the first person to use the term 'horsepower'?

6   Which Scottish mathematician and physicist gave his name to a temperature scale beginning with absolute zero?

7   In which year did Henry Morton Stanley greet David Livingstone with the words 'Doctor Livingstone, I presume'?

8   Who won Glasgow Hillhead for the SDP in 1982?

9   Who is the Baron of Renfrew?

10 What type of vehicle is Kirkpatrick Macmillan credited with having invented?

11 In which county was Thomas Telford born?

12 Which Scottish-born naval hero became known as the 'father of the US Navy'?

13 Who was the last member of the Royal Family to be born in Scotland?

14 Which Scot became the UK's first Labour Prime Minister?

15 The entrepreneur James McGill founded McGill University in which city?

ANSWERS

1. Keir Hardie 2. The womens' suffrage movement 3. Scurvy 4. Sir Nicholas Fairbairn 5. James Watt 6. Lord Kelvin 7. 1871 8. Roy Jenkins 9. Prince Charles 10. The pedal bicycle 11. Dumfries and Galloway 12. John Paul Jones 13. Princess Margaret 14. Ramsay MacDonald 15. Montreal

1 *Death and Doctor Hornbrook* was the first satire by which much-loved writer?

2 Who wrote *The Wind in the Willows?*

3 In the ballad 'Mary Hamilton goes to Edinburgh', why does she go there?

4 The smuggler captain Dirk Hatteraick features in which Sir Walter Scott novel?

5 Who wrote *Prester John?*

6 Which poet, author of 'The Bruce', is commonly regarded as the Father of Scottish poetry?

7 What name was Hugh MacDiarmid born with?

8 Who fled the plague in Edinburgh in 1568 to his father's estate in Forfarshire and compiled the work of the makars, the Scots poets of the 15th and 16th century, into the manuscript that bears his name?

9 Which poet and humorist played Buster Bloodvessel in 'The Magical Mystery Tour'?

10 Whose Collected Poems 1967–1984 is entitled *Dreaming Frankenstein?*

11 Where is Burns' birthplace?

12 How old was Lewis Grassic Gibbon at his death following an operation on an ulcer?

13 Which Glaswegian poet translated Rostand's 'Cyrano de Bergerac'?

14 What was Irvine Welsh's second published book?

15 Who wrote the novel *Tunes Of Glory*, later adapted into a film?

ANSWERS

1. Robert Burns 2. Kenneth Grahame 3. To be hanged for killing a baby 4. *Guy Mannering* 5. John Buchan 6. John Barbour 7. Christopher Murray Grieve 8. George Bannatyne 9. Ivor Cutler 10. Liz Lochhead 11. Alloway, near Ayr 12. 34 13. Edwin Morgan 14. *The Acid House* 15. James Kennaway

37

GENERAL KNOWLEDGE

1 Where did the Highland chiefs assemble in 1746, after the defeat at Culloden, only to receive a message of farewell from the Young Pretender?

2 What is unusual about Soay sheep, which live on the Hebridean island of Hirta?

3 What is Avern jelly?

4 In which month is the Edinburgh Folk Festival held?

5 What does 'Ban' mean in a place name?

6 Why was Eaglesham, Renfrewshire, in the news in 1941?

7 Which 1958 by-election was the first with campaign broadcasting coverage allowed by Parliament?

8 What was the date of the first election of the Scottish Parliament?

9 When will the purpose-built home of the Parliament open?

10 A 100-metre tower is part of a plan to build a £71.5 million science complex. Where?

11 Glasgow city council decided to return what Native American artefact in 1998?

12 A small portion of which EU country was designated British territory in 1999 in order to try two Lockerbie bomb suspects under Scots law?

13 How many Scottish seats are there in the Westminster Parliament?

14 At the time of the first Scottish Parliamentary elections in May 1999, how many UK Cabinet Ministers were Westminster MPs for Scottish seats?

15 What nationality are the two prime suspects of the Lockerbie bombing?

ANSWERS

1. Ruthven Barracks 2. They are the only truly wild sheep in Britain 3. Jelly or jam made with wild strawberries 4. March 5. White 6. It was where Rudolf Hess crash-landed 7. Kelvingrove 8. May 6, 1999 9. 2001 10. Pacific Quay, Glasgow 11. A Lakota Sioux ghost shirt 12. Netherlands 13. 72 14. Six 15. Libyan

1 What is the largest island in Loch Lomond?

2 Which town lies at the western end of Hadrian's Wall?

3 Which is Scotland's longest glen?

4 Deer Abbey lies 10 miles north of which large town?

5 Where is Napier University?

6 Which is the smallest and most southerly of the Small Isles?

7 On the shores of which loch is Lochgilphead situated?

8 Which is the most southerly of the Munros?

9 What does 'The Trossachs' mean?

10 Which is Orkney's second largest island?

11 Which castle, 13 miles north of Inverurie, has five steeples, one for each of the families who have lived there since the 13th century?

12 What is the name of the basalt rock, home to millions of nesting sea-birds, rising 350 feet out of the sea three miles east of North Berwick?

13 Which town in Argyll was originally known as Kinlochkilkerran, until it was renamed in the 17th century by the Earl of Argyll?

14 Which two towns or cities are connected by the A94?

15 What is the name of the tiny village at the south-western tip of Loch Ness?

ANSWERS

1. Inchmurrin 2. Bowness-on-Solway 3. Glen Lyon: 30 miles/48 km 4. Peterhead 5. Edinburgh 6. Muck 7. Loch Fyne 8. Ben Lomond 9. Either 'bristly country', or 'crossing place' 10. Hoy 11. Fyvie Castle 12. Bass Rock 13. Campbeltown 14. Aberdeen and Dundee 15. Fort Augustus

HISTORY

1   In which year did the Union of the Crowns (Scottish and English) take place?

2   The first Jacobite Rising took place in which year?

3   In what year was the Tay Railway Bridge blown down, killing 75 people?

4   Malcolm III was known as 'Canmore'. What does Canmore mean?

5   King Charles I surrendered to Scottish forces in which year?

6   What was the name of the plan to establish a Scottish colony in Panama in 1698?

7   Which process of rural upheaval began in 1785?

8   Where did the Earl of Mar raise the Stewart standard in September 1715?

9   Whom did Queen Mary marry following the murder of Lord Darnley?

10 What was the common name for the doctrine that John Knox brought back to Scotland in 1559 and which formed the basis of the reformed faith for over 70 years?

11 What was the name of the group of nobles who banded together in 1557 to oppose French influence and promote the reformed religion?

12 Where did James IV die?

13 How many MacDonalds were killed in the Glencoe massacre?

14 In which year did the National Party of Scotland merge with the right-wing Scottish Party to form the SNP?

15 Who became Secretary of State for Scotland in the 1995 cabinet reshuffle?

ANSWERS

1. 1603 2. 1715 3. 1879 4. Bighead 5. 1650 6. The Darien Scheme 7. The Highland Clearances 8. Braemar Castle 9. The Earl of Bothwell, widely believed to be Darnley's murderer 10. The Scot's Confession 11. Lords of the Congregation 12. Flodden Field 13. 38 14. 1934 15. Michael Forsyth

4

1 What does the expression 'kerry fisted' mean?

2 What is the name of the comic publisher based in Dundee?

3 How long is the border between Scotland and England?

4 In the army, what do the letters RHF stand for?

5 Which number regiment is the Gordon Highlanders?

6 The word whisky comes from the Gaelic expression 'uisge beatha', or 'usquebaugh'. What does this literally mean?

7 Who are the monarch's bodyguard in Scotland?

8 What are natives of the Orkney Islands known as?

9 Which is the oldest Scottish university?

10 Which town is supposed to appear every 100 years for one day?

11 What is the third possible verdict, apart from 'guilty' or 'not guilty', that a Scottish jury can bring in?

12 When is Burns' Night?

13 What is the minimum height of a Munro?

14 What name is used for mountains between 2500 and 2999 feet?

15 What was the Roman name for Scotland?

ANSWERS

1. Left-handed 2. DC Thompson 3. 108 miles/174 km 4. Royal Highland Fusiliers 5. 92nd 6. Water of life 7. The Royal Company of Archers 8. Orcadians 9. St Andrews 10. Brigadoon 11. Not proven 12. January 25 13. 3000 feet/914 m 14. Corbetts 15. Caledonia

TV & ENTERTAINMENT

1 Who was the compere of *The White Heather Club* on TV?

2 Which Scottish singer performed the theme song to the Bond film *For Your Eyes Only?*

3 Which Scottish singer performed the theme song to the Bond film *The Man With The Golden Gun?*

4 Who played Private Fraser in *Dad's Army?*

5 In which Hitchcock film did John Laurie play a crofter?

6 Which pop singer teamed up with Kenny Dalglish to make a multi-million pound bid for Celtic in 1998?

7 Plans to build Scotland's largest cinema screen were announced in 1998 for which Glasgow location?

8 Who was Robin Hall's partner in a successful folk-singing duo?

9 Which famous radio programme did Kathleen Garscadden first arrange?

10 How did 5SC achieve fame in 1923?

11 In which year was John Reith named Director General of the BBC?

12 What was unusual about the producer of the first radio drama broadcast in Gaelic in 1933?

13 When and why did Scottish radio programmes merge with the BBC Home Serivce?

14 From which city was Scotland's first radio broadcast in Gaelic transmitted?

15 What special broadcasting event took place on October 13, 1924?

ANSWERS

1. Andy Stewart 2. Sheena Easton 3. Lulu 4. John Laurie 5. *The Thirty-Nine Steps* 6. Jim Kerr 7. Pacific Quay 8. Jimmy McGregor 9. 'Woman's Hour' 10. As Glasgow's first radio station 11. 1927 12. He spoke no Gaelic 13. September 1939, at the outbreak of the Second World War 14. Aberdeen 15. First election broadcast by Labour Prime Minister Ramsay MacDonald

1 Colin McRae is a leading performer in which sport?

2 Who is the only Scot to have won a stage in the Tour de France?

3 Which football club is nicknamed 'The Buddies'?

4 Which Formula One racing team launched Jim Clark's career?

5 For which rugby union club does Marcus di Rollo play?

6 After their careers with Celtic and Rangers, Jimmie Johnstone and Willie Henderson joined different clubs in the same English city – which?

7 Which football team has the largest ground in Britain?

8 Against whom did Willie Henderson make his debut for Scotland in 1962, winning 3-2 away from home?

9 How many times did Jim Clark win the world championship?

10 Where would you find a hogline?

11 Which team won the Scottish League in its first two seasons, 1890–91 and '91–'92 (the first year jointly with Rangers)?

12 Who won the 400 metres gold medal in the 1924 Olympics?

13 What is the name of the Edinburgh rugby union 'super team'?

14 What is the name of the Glasgow rugby union 'super team'?

15 Who was the captain of the 1974 World Cup squad?

ANSWERS

1. Rallying 2. Robert Millar 3. St Mirren 4. Ecurie Ecosse 5. Watsonians 6. Sheffield (Johnstone – United, Henderson – Wednesday) 7. Celtic 8. Wales 9. two (1963 and 1965) 10. In a game of curling 11. Dumbarton 12. Eric Liddel 13. Edinburgh Reivers 14. Glasgow Caledonians 15. Billy Bremner

PEOPLE

1 Which famous Scottish botanist had a fir tree named after him?

2 Which former chairman of British Steel headed the National Coal Board under Prime Minister Margaret Thatcher?

3 In which East Lothian town was the 16th-century religious reformer John Knox born?

4 Who designed the earliest surviving part of the University of Edinburgh, known as Old College or Old Quad?

5 Who was the first General Manager of the BBC?

6 Whom did Oscar Wilde sue for libel in 1895?

7 Who was the surgeon who introduced antiseptics to the medical world?

8 Who became the youngest ever Scottish MP when he was elected in 1965?

9 Who is the deaf percussionist who is an Honorary Doctor of Music at Aberdeen University?

10 Who invented the adhesive postage stamp?

11 What financial institution was founded by William Paterson in 1694?

12 Who invented television?

13 Which statesman was drowned when HMS *Hampshire* went down in 1916, mined off the Orkney Islands?

14 Which recent Chancellor of the Exchequer was born in Lerwick in the Shetland Isles?

15 Which saint was Queen of Scotland between 1286 and 1292?

ANSWERS

1. David Douglas 2. Sir Ian McGregor 3. Haddington 4. Robert Adam 5. John Reith 6. The Marquis of Queensbury 7. Joseph Lister 8. David Steel 9. Evelyn Glennie 10. James Chalmers 11. The Bank of England 12. John Logie Baird 13. Lord Kitchener 14. Norman Lamont 15. Saint Margaret

1   What does the old word 'mellison' mean?

2   Who, in the famous ballad, did Lord Douglas and his seven sons fight?

3   To where did Burns intend to emigrate, publishing his first collection of poems to raise the fare, before changing his mind when it received favourable reviews and modest financial success?

4   Which Orcadian poet was, with his wife, Kafka's first translator into English?

5   Which historical figure was the author of a collection of poems called 'Bittersweet Within My Heart'?

6   Whose novel *A Dark and Distant Shore* brought favourable comparisons with *Gone With The Wind*?

7   In which continent is Conan Doyle's 'Lost World'?

8   Who wrote the 15th-century epic 'Wallace'?

9   Which novel features Detective Sergeant Bruce Robertson, a corrupt policeman whose only source of conscience is his own anus?

10   In which year was Robert Louis Stevenson born?

11   Born around 1460, which poet was active at the court of James IV?

12   Who wrote the influential but underrated science fiction novel *A Voyage To Arcturus*?

13   What is the title of the first novel in 'A Scots Quair'?

14   What was Sir Walter Scott's first published novel?

15   What was the real name of the Hebridean story-teller known as The Coddy?

ANSWERS

1. A curse 2. Lord William 3. Jamaica 4. Edwin Muir 5. Mary, Queen of Scots 6. Reay Tannahill 7. South America 8. Blind Harry 9. Irvine Welsh's *Filth* 10. 1850 11. William Dunbar 12. David Lindsay 13. *Sunset Song* 14. *Waverley* 15. John MacPherson

GENERAL KNOWLEDGE

1 What foreign country has historically had the greatest influence on Scottish cuisine?

2 On which date did the Scottish Parliament officially open?

3 Where will the new purpose-built home of the Parliament be located?

4 What does 'Beg' mean in a place name?

5 At the time of the first Scottish Parliamentary elections in May 1999, how many Westminster seats did the SNP hold?

6 What is 'fat-kail'?

7 Whom did the German astronomer Kepler regard as the greatest mathematician of his generation?

8 What is a 'niffer'?

9 What is the temporary home of the Scottish Parliament?

10 Which clan supported the famous minstrel Roderick Morison?

11 What is 'yowdendrift'?

12 If someone is havering, what is he or she doing?

13 Where is the Land o' Burns Centre?

14 Which river runs through Patna?

15 What is a 'pingle'?

ANSWERS

1. France 2. 1 July 3. Holyrood, Edinburgh 4. Small 5. Six 6. Broth made with fatty stock 7. John Napier 8. An exchange or bargain 9. Church of Scotland General Assembly Hall 10. MacLeod 11. Wind-driven snow 12. Drivelling 13. Alloway 14. Doon 15. Combat or struggle

1 The Little Minch separates Lewis, North Uuist and South Uuist from which other island?

2 What is the easternmost point on the Scottish mainland?

3 Which town or city is famous for 'Jam, Jute and Journalism'?

4 Which is the 'Granite City'?

5 What is Mons Meg?

6 After Loch Lomond and Loch Ness, which is the next largest inland, freshwater loch?

7 In which city is the Caird Hall?

8 On which river does Dumfries stand?

9 What are the names of Glasgow's two main railway stations?

10 What is the southernmost point on the Scottish mainland?

11 Which loch is situated beneath Ben Nevis?

12 Where is The Old Man of Hoy?

13 What is the name of the range of hills that stretches for 40 miles/64 km along the northern side of the Firth of Forth, north-east of Stirling?

14 What are the names of Edinburgh's two railway stations?

15 What marks the place in Edinburgh's Royal Mile where the Tolbooth Prison stood?

ANSWERS

1. Skye 2. Buchan Ness 3. Dundee 4. Aberdeen 5. A gun 6. Loch Awe 7. Dundee 8. River Nith 9. Queen Street and Central 10. Mull of Galloway 11. Loch Linnhe 12. The Orkneys 13. The Ochils 14. Waverley and Haymarket 15. The Heart of Midlothian

HISTORY

1 Where did Jacobite forces under Bonnie Prince Charlie first raise the Stuart standard in 1745?

2 In which year was the Second Covenant signed?

3 The Proscription Act was repealed in 1782. What had it proscribed (or prohibited)?

4 What was the name of the particularly brutal estate factor of the Countess of Sutherland, who performed some of the most notorious of the Highland Clearances?

5 Why were the Picts so called?

6 Christian I, father of Margaret, the subject of a proposed arranged marriage with the future King James III, was the king of which country?

7 Who succeeded Charles II as king of Scotland?

8 How far south did Prince Charles Edward Stewart reach in his advance into England?

9 When was the battle of Flodden Field?

10 Where was Mary, Queen of Scots born?

11 Where was the battleship *Royal Oak* scuttled by the Germans just after the outbreak of World War II, with the loss of 833 lives?

12 What sort of Scottish historical document was discovered in Lubeck, Germany, in 1998?

13 How many Scottish seats did the Tories lose in the 1997 general election?

14 How old was the Duke of Cumberland at the Battle of Culloden?

15 How old was the Bonnie Prince Charlie at the Battle of Culloden?

ANSWERS

1. Glenfinnan 2. 1638 3. The wearing of Highland dress 4. Patrick Sellar 5. Because of their tattoos 6. Denmark 7. James VII 8. Derby 9. 1513 10. Linlithgow 11. Scapa Flow 12. A letter written by William Wallace 13. Eleven 14. Twenty-five 15. Twenty-six

1. Which school in Scotland did Tony Blair attend?

2. On which day is the Ne'erday Bonfire in Biggar?

3. Which Dukes are also Dukes of Chatelherault in France?

4. Where could you attend the Burry Man and Ferry Fair every August?

5. The name of which Orkney island means 'high island' in Norse?

6. What is a 'brock'?

7. Who made a world-famous unscheduled flight to Scotland on May 11, 1941?

8. What did Tony Blair switch on at the Forth Rail Bridge on November 14, 1998?

9. What connects Kelvingrove Art Gallery, Glasgow, and the Battle of Wounded Knee?

10. Why was Scottish Power's 1998 merger with PacifiCorp significant?

11. Who represents Dunfermline East in the Westminster Parliament?

12. In 1998 Glasgow city council returned a Native American ghost shirt to the Lakota Sioux. From which touring group had they bought it in 1891?

13. In which year did the Royal Bank of Scotland first make profits of more than £1 billion?

14. The Norse term 'haar' means what?

15. What is 'clitter'?

ANSWERS

1. Fettes, in Edinburgh 2. December 31 3. Hamilton 4. Queensferry 5. Hoy 6. A stone tower 7. Rudolf Hess 8. A digital clock counting down to the Millennium 9. A Lakota Sioux shirt that the gallery returned to Native Americans in 1998 10. It was the first time a British company bought a US utility 11. Gordon Brown 12. Buffalo Bill's Wild West Show 13. 1998 14. Sea mists that roll in to eastern Scotland 15. Rock fragments on mountain slopes, formed by frequent freezing and thawing

TV & ENTERTAINMENT

1 Name the film star connection in the following films: *Looking after Jo-Jo, Ravenous* and *Poor Things*.

2 Which multi-talented American performer encouraged folk singers Robin Hall and Jimmy McGregor early in their careers?

3 In which year was the first broadcast of the television series 'Dr Finlay's Casebook'?

4 Where is Radio Highland based?

5 In which year were the first BBC colour TV broadcasts in Scotland?

6 What was 'The McFlannels Rub Along'?

7 'The Queen of the Clyde', a 1967 documentary, concerned what?

8 'Lex Again' was a vehicle for which comedian?

9 What were Kirkwall and Lerwick the first to receive, in 1929?

10 Andy Stewart introduced which live programme, first broadcast in 1958?

11 In which year was the first radio outside broadcast in Scotland?

12 Jimmy Logan, Primrose Milligan and Eddie Fraser starred in which variety series?

13 In which year was the first Gaelic Service outside broadcast?

14 What distinction did Elizabeth Adair hold?

15 The first broadcast of which long-running television programme was made from the Locarno Ballroom, Glasgow, on August 29, 1952?

ANSWERS

1. Robert Carlyle 2. Paul Robeson 3. 1958 4. Inverness 5. 1969 6. A radio drama series based on the life of a Glasgow family 7. The building and launch of the QE2 8. Lex MacLean 9. The first BBC television transmission 10. 'The White Heather Club' 11. 1923 12. 'It's All Yours' 13. 1963 14. She was the first female radio presenter in Scotland 15. 'Come Dancing'

SPORT

1　Against whom did Jimmy Johnstone make his debut for Scotland in October, 1964, losing 3-2 away from home?

2　Which Scottish sport was first contested for medals in the 1998 Olympics?

3　Of the 25 Grand Prix circuits, how many did Jim Clark win during his career?

4　Whom did the SRU appoint in early 1999 to chair an independent review of the rugby in Scotland?

5　Who beat Celtic 2-1 after extra time in the 1970 European Cup final?

6　Who is Scotland's most capped rugby international?

7　Name the racing driver, tipped to be a future Formula One star, who was born to an Edinburgh ice-cream making family.

8　Which club was formed following the amalgamation of Alpha and Glencairn, and was originally known as Wee Alpha before taking its present name in 1886?

9　What position does New Zealand-born John Leslie play on the Scottish international rugby side?

10　Which international water-polo player went on to pursue a successful television career as a presenter and actor?

11　Which player scored a hat-trick against Spain in 1957, helping Scotland to qualify for the 1958 World Cup finals in Sweden?

12　Which top English rugby team was poised to take over London Scottish in early 1999?

13　Name Alan Hansen's brother, who won 2 caps for Scotland in 1972?

14　A picture of which darts player once erroneously appeared as a 'Top of the Pops' backdrop during a song by Dexy's Midnight Runners?

15　Who became the temporary Scotland manager following Jock Stein's death after the World Cup qualifier against Wales for the 1986 finals?

ANSWERS

1. Wales 2. Curling 3. All 25 4. Lord Mackay of Strathfern 5. Feyenoord 6. Scott Hastings 7. Dario Franchitti 8. Motherwell 9. Centre 10. Ross Davidson 11. Jackie Mudie 12. Bristol 13. John 14. Jockie Wilson (it should have been soul singer Jackie Wilson) 15. Alex Ferguson

PEOPLE

1   Who invented the waterproof raincoat?

2   Who is the Earl of Carrick?

3   Who was the mathematician born in 1550 at Merchiston Castle, Edinburgh, who invented logarithms?

4   Which engineer planned the Ellesmere and Caledonian canals?

5   Who was the first European to discover the Victoria Falls on the Zambesi?

6   Who wrote the songs *Keep Right on to the End of the Road* and *Roamin' in the Gloamin'*?

7   How many Scottish-born Prime Ministers have there been this century?

8   What was the name of the sailor born in Largo, Fife in 1676 who inspired the writing of one of the world's most famous books?

9   Who was the progressive educationist born in Kingsmuir, Fife, who founded Summerhill School in 1927?

10   Who was the Borders-born explorer of Africa who was drowned aged 35 in 1806?

11   Name the Celtic Football Club chairman who announced in 1998 his intention to sell his share in the club and to return to Canada.

12   What is SNP leader Alex Salmond's Westminster consistuency?

13   At the time of the elections to the Scottish Parliament in 1999, what Cabinet post did Alistair Darling hold?

14   What is the constituency of Menzies Campbell?

15   Which Roman soldier and political leader is credited with inventing the term 'Pict'?

ANSWERS

1. Charles Macintosh 2. Prince Charles 3. John Napier 4. Thomas Telford 5. David Livingstone 6. Harry Lauder 7. 4 (Balfour, Campbell-Bannerman, MacDonald and Blair. Bonar-Law was born in Canada, and both Macmillan and Alec Douglas Home were born in London) 8. Alexander Selkirk 9. A.S. Neill 10. Mungo Park 11. Fergus McCann 12. Banff and Buchan 13. Chief Secretary to the Treasury 14. Fife North East 15. Agricola

MUSIC & LITERATURE

1 In the famous ballad, what was Janet's fate?

2 Who wrote *The Guns of Navarone?*

3 Whose first collection of short stories, published in 1983, was called 'Not Not While The Giro'?

4 Who wrote the novels on which the TV series 'Dr Finlay's Casebook' was based?

5 Which early 19th-century author wrote the political novels *The Member* and *The Radical?*

6 With which form of writing would you associate Gavin Douglas?

7 Who wrote the classic trilogy 'A Scots Quair'?

8 Which Lanarkshire-born novelist wrote *The Cone Gatherers* and *Fergus Lamont?*

9 Which Edinburgh-born novelist became a DBE in 1993?

10 Which Scottish novelist, born in 1934, is also an accomplished artist and designer?

11 Which Glasgow-born novelist who originally trained as an accountant has written over 100 books, many of them fictionalised accounts of Scottish history?

12 Who created the tough Glaswegian cop Jack Laidlaw?

13 Which Edinburgh-born author of over 70 books was adopted as the 'Mother' of a tribe in Botswana in the 1960s?

14 Whose novels include *The Last Enchantment, Touch Not The Cat* and *The Crystal Cave?*

15 What does the M stand for in J M Barrie?

ANSWERS

1. To be burnt on a bonfire because she was pregnant and unmarried 2. Alistair McLean 3. James Kelman 4. A. J. Cronin 5. John Galt 6. Poetry 7. Lewis Grassic Gibbon 8. Robin Jenkins 9. Muriel Spark 10. Alasdair Gray 11. Nigel Tranter 12. William McIlvanney 13. Naomi Mitchison 14. Mary Stewart 15. Matthew

GENERAL KNOWLEDGE

1 What, in Medieval times, was a mormaer?

2 When did Prince Albert buy the site where Balmoral Castle was later built?

3 Which flower was named after the Duke of Cumberland after his victory at Culloden?

4 In which city are most of the works by architect Archibald Simpson?

5 Of what rock is the Stone of Destiny composed?

6 By how may pence in the pound is the new Scottish Parliament allowed to vary income tax?

7 What £660,000 vehicle broke down on the banks of Loch Lomond in May 1998?

8 What is forming the centre-piece of a new cruise-ship and conference terminal in Leith?

9 A £2.3 billion plant in Dunfermline was shelved by which company in June 1998?

10 Which company cloned Dolly the sheep?

11 What did SNP leader Alex Salmond condemn as 'unpardonable folly' in April 1999?

12 How many Highlands and Islands constituencies are there in the new Scottish Parliament?

13 Which four universities combined to develop the world's first System Level Integration Institute?

14 Which Scottish company operates 17 per cent of the UK's buses and trains?

15 How many members sit in the Scottish Parliament?

ANSWERS

1. A Great Steward 2. 1852 3. Sweet William 4. Aberdeen 5. Red sandstone 6. 3p 7. A new mobile cinema 8. The royal yacht *Britannia* 9. Hyundai 10. PPL Therapeutics 11. NATO bombing of Yugoslavia 12. Eight 13. Glasgow, Edinburgh, Heriot-Watt and Strathclyde 14. Stagecoach 15. 129

PLACES

1   What is the westernmost point on the Scottish mainland?

2   Where is the 'whisky triangle'?

3   What is the easternmost mainland town in Scotland?

4   Where is Mons Meg?

5   Which town is the main commercial centre of the Forth Valley?

6   Which is the largest town on the Firth of Clyde coast?

7   In which town is the Smith Art Gallery and Museum?

8   What is the chief town on Mull?

9   What is the county town of Angus?

10 The Great Glen stretches from Inverness to which town?

11 To which saint is the cathedral in Kirkwall dedicated?

12 Where is Sumburgh Airport?

13 Which controversial art gallery is divided into four levels named Fire, Earth, Water and Air?

14 What does Ailsa Craig mean in Gaelic?

15 In which street is Edinburgh's Royal Lyceum Theatre?

ANSWERS

1. Ardnamurchan Point 2. Speyside 3. Peterhead 4. Edinburgh Castle 5. Falkirk 6. Ayr 7. Stirling 8. Tobermory 9. Forfar 10. Fort William 11. St Magnus 12. Lerwick 13. The Gallery of Modern Art in Glasgow 14. Fairy Rock 15. Grindlay Street

HISTORY

1 In what year was the Tay Road Bridge opened?

2 Which English king sat on the throne during the Jacobite Rising of 1745?

3 Where did Prince Charles Edward Stewart die?

4 What was the name of Mary Queen of Scots' horse?

5 How many seats did the SNP gain in the 1997 general election?

6 In which year did Agricola make his first incursion into what is now Scotland?

7 For how many years did Macbeth reign?

8 How old was Mary, Queen of Scots when she became Queen?

9 Who was the last King of the House of Canmore?

10 Bennachie, located north-west of Aberdeen, is the likely site of which ancient battle?

11 Who was elected a guardian of the Kingdom along with Robert the Bruce after the Battle of Falkirk?

12 When did the English siege of Sterling begin?

13 In which year did the Scots defeat the English at Mytton?

14 In which year did Edward III of England sign the Treaty of Northampton, recognising Scotland as an independent nation?

15 What post did Archibald Douglas hold in the 1330s?

ANSWERS

1. 1966 2. George II 3. Rome 4. Black Agnes 5. Three 6. AD 62 7. Seventeen 8. Six days 9. Alexander III 10. Mons Graupius 11. John Comyn 12. 1313 13. 1319 14. 1328 15. Scottish regent

TRIVIA

1 What is the name of the brown-fleeced sheep native to Scotland but now a rare breed?

2 According to tradition, when was the last wolf in Scotland killed?

3 Who represents Livingston in the Westminster Parliament?

4 What is *Caledonia evansi*?

5 What is the 'Sweetheart Abbey' in southern Scotland made out of?

6 How did the Strath of Kildonan make the news in 1896?

7 What does the word 'Kyle' mean?

8 Is Loch Morar a fresh- or salt-water loch?

9 Why would you find 'twitchers' in the Solway Firth?

10 Gold mined in which hills was used to make the Scottish crown?

11 What is *Ligusticum scotica*?

12 What disaster occurred in Culbin, Morayshire, in 1694?

13 What are 'scaurs'?

14 What is the Latin name of the Scots rose?

15 The sands at Morar consist largely of what?

ANSWERS

1. Moorit 2. 1743 3. Robin Cook 4. A species of spider 5. Pink sand - new red sandstone 6. There was a gold rush there 7. A narrow channel of water between an island and the mainland 8. Fresh 9. 'Twitchers' (bird-lovers) are attracted by the profusion of bird life 10. Lowther Hills 11. A species of lovage found along Scottish coasts 12. A complete estate was buried under sand 13. Boulder clay deposits in the Solway Firth 14. *Rosa pimpinelli folia* 15. Silica

TV & ENTERTAINMENT

1   In which year was the first rugby international broadcast from Murrayfield?

2   Tony Roper and Barbara Rafferty appeared on which comedy which premiered in September 1990?

3   Who was the highest-profile guest to be a guest on 'Open to Question' in 1984?

4   The Kirkintilloch Children's Choir performed on which famous radio braodcast?

5   'Tutti Frutti' won 13 BAFTA nominations in which year?

6   Who plays Michael Jardine in 'Taggart'?

7   What was the subject of the special edition of the *Radio Times* on March 7, 1952?

8   Which famous broadcaster/writer was born in Reykjavik and moved to Scotland when he was nine months old?

9   Ron Bain, Tony Roper and Elaine C Smith were among the performers on which TV comedy?

10 In which year did the 'Stanley Baxter Show' first appear?

11 High Definition TV was first demonstrated in Scotland in which year?

12 From where in London was the first television broadcast using the Baird system?

13 Who played Lynne McNeil in 'Take the High Road'?

14 In which year did BBC2 service come to Scotland?

15 Which TV and radio actor toured with his one-man show 'Bozzy', as James Boswell?

ANSWERS

1. 1927 2. 'Rab C Nesbit' 3. HRH Princess Anne 4. The Victory Edition of Scottish Half Hour on 10 May 1945 5. 1988 6. James MacPherson 7. 'Television comes to Scotland' 8. Magnus Magnusson 9. 'Naked Video' 10. 1967 11. 1988 12. Alexandra Palace 13. Gillian McNeill 14. 1963 15. David McKail

SPORT

1　In which sport would you use a caman?

2　Which team did Denis Law join when Manchester United gave him a free transfer in 1973?

3　How many times did Jackie Stewart win the world championship?

4　What was the famous scoreline in the Scottish Cup first round tie between Arbroath and Bon Accord in 1885?

5　In which sport would you 'soop'?

6　What is the name of John Leslie's brother and fellow rugby international?

7　Who were the first winners of the Scottish Premier Division?

8　In 1567, Mary, Queen of Scots drew resentment by playing which sport soon after the death of her husband?

9　Which course did Henry Cotton describe as a 'golfer's paradise'?

10　From which Scottish club did Tottenham buy Steve Archibald in 1980

11　At which ski resort would you find Butchart's Corrie?

12　Who plays at Ochilview Park?

13　When does the season for stalking red deer begin?

14　Which team was Jim Clark driving for when he won his two world championships?

15　Which was the first season of the Scottish Premier Division?

ANSWERS

1. Shinty (the name of the stick) 2. Manchester City 3. 3 (1969, 1971 and 1973) 4. 36-0
5. Curling (to sweep with the broom) 6. Martin 7. Rangers 8. Golf 9. Machrie 10. Aberdeen
11. Glenshee 12. Stenhousemuir 13. 1 July 14. Lotus 15. 1975-6

59

PEOPLE

1   What was Ramsay MacDonald's first name?

2   Which MP for Glasgow Govan was found innocent of 1997 election irregularities?

3   Which Scottish naturalist wrote the text to accompany John James Audubon's paintings in *Ornithological Biographies*?

4   Who wrote *The Scenery of Scotland*?

5   Who is MP for Ross, Skye and Inverness West?

6   The 14th-century author John Barbor was archdeacon of which church?

7   How old was Robert Louis Stevenson when he died?

8   Sir Robert Sibbald is known as 'the father of' which branch of Scottish science?

9   Which 15th-century poet was a Dunfermline schoolmaster?

10 The 16th-century playwright Sir William Alexander had which title?

11 Who is the only non-Labour MP to represent Edinburgh?

12 How many non-Labour MPs represent Glasgow?

13 In which field of science would you associate James Hutton?

14 Which Scottish naturalist gave his name to two species of spider?

15 Which party had a larger share of the popular Scottish vote in the 1997 general election: Conservatives or Liberal Democrats?

ANSWERS

1. James 2. Mohammed Sarwar 3. William McGillivray 4. Geologist Sir Archibald Geikie 5. Charles Kennedy 6. St Machar's, Aberdeen 7. 44 8. Botany 9. Gavin Douglas 10. Earl of Stirling 11. Donald Gorrie 12. None 13. Geology 14. W Evans 15. Conservatives (17.5% vs 13%)

1 Macbeth is hailed by the second witch as Thane of what?

2 Which Gaelic-speaking poet was born and raised on the Isle of Lewis?

3 Which author of a classic children's book was born in Edinburgh in 1859?

4 Which poet and novelist was shortlisted for the Booker prize with his novel *Beside The Ocean Of Time?*

5 What is the surname of George MacDonald Fraser's Private, the dirtiest soldier in the world?

6 Who wrote a sequence of poems called 'Poems for Angus' following the death of a friend?

7 Who created the comic hero Para Handy?

8 Which poet, born in Inchinnan, Renfrewshire in 1942, has won numerous literary prizes and gained especial praise for 'Elegies', a collection of poems written after the death of his wife in 1981?

9 Which 'Scottish Chaucerian' of the 15th-century wrote 'The Testament of Cresseid'?

10 Who wrote the novel *Cloud Howe?*

11 Which Glaswegian poet's collections include 'Standing Female Nude', 'Selling Manhattan' and 'Mean Time', for which she won the Whitbread and Forward poetry prizes?

12 What is the name of Iain M Banks' future world, in which most of his science fiction is set?

13 Which 19th-century historian wrote 'Sartor Resartus' and a highly idealised history of the French Revolution?

14 What is the name of Ian Rankin's detective?

15 Which writer created the badly dressed portrait painter and amateur detective Johnson Johnson?

ANSWERS

1. Cawdor 2. Iain Crichton Smith 3. Kenneth Grahame 4. George Mackay Brown 5. MacAuslan 6. Norman MacCaig 7. Neil Munro 8. Douglas Dunn 9. Robert Henryson 10. Lewis Grassic Gibbon 11. Carol Anne Duffy 12. The Culture 13. Thomas Carlyle 14. Inspector John Rebus 15. Dorothy Dunnett

GENERAL KNOWLEDGE

1   What does 'Dubh' mean in a place name?

2   When will the Bear Gates of Tranquair House reopen?

3   Stirling Castle is built on what type of geological feature?

4   Gleneagles has been the home of which family for more than 800 years?

5   What is the name of the Duke of Atholl's private standing army?

6   The West Highland rail line runs from where to where?

7   Which river discharges more water than any other in Britain?

8   In which year was the last peer of the realm executed?

9   In which year was Ullapool founded?

10   The Macdonald of Glenaladale erected which famous monument in 1815?

11   What does Dalwhinnie mean?

12   As late as 1900 the Marquess of Breadalbane could ride from east to west for how many miles without leaving his own property?

13   In the 18th and 19th centuries what did Glasgow and Edinburgh merchants store in 'howfs'?

14   Younger Botainc Garden lies in the grounds of which stately home?

15   What are 'merry-dancers'?

ANSWERS

1. Black 2. When a Stuart reigns once more 3. An extinct volcano 4. Haldane 5. The Atholl Highlanders 6. Glasgow to Fort William 7. Tay 8. 1747 (the 11th Lord Lovat) 9. 1788 10. The Glenfinnan Monument 11. Dell of the meeting 12. 100 miles 13. Oysters 14. Benmore House 15. Northern lights

PLACES

1. What is the northernmost point on the Scottish mainland?
2. Whose statue is on the top of the column in George Square, Glasgow?
3. What is the largest place on the Isle of Islay?
4. On the south-western corner of which Edinburgh bridge is the statue of Greyfriars Bobby?
5. In which Glasgow street is the Theatre Royal?
6. In which town does the ancient ceremony of Fireballs take place on New Year's Eve?
7. Which town lies at the centre of the Argyll coastal region known as Lorn?
8. Where is Dewar's Whisky produced?
9. Tantallon Castle was the stronghold of which branch of the Douglases?
10. Where would you find Jenny Batter's Hole?
11. The Royal Botanical Garden, Edinburgh, is Britain's second-oldest botanical garden. Where is the oldest?
12. How tall is the Old Man of Hoy: a)450 feet, b)526 feet, c)609 feet
13. A new Gazetteer of Scotland will be completed in 2000, replacing the last one. When was it compiled?
14. Near which town would you find the village of California?
15. The place name Drymen derives from a Celtic word meaning what?

ANSWERS

1. Dunnet Head 2. Sir Walter Scott 3. Port Ellen 4. George IV Bridge 5. Hope Street 6. Stonehaven 7. Oban 8. Perth 9. The Red Douglases 10. Arbroath Abbey 11. Oxford 12. a)450 feet 13. 1885 14. Falkirk 15. Ridge or knoll

HISTORY

1 Whom did Mary Queen of Scots succeed to the throne?

2 Which Scottish king was nicknamed 'The Maiden'?

3 Who led the Scots in the Battle of Dunbar against Cromwell in 1650?

4 As whom was Prince Charles Edward Stewart disguised when he escaped to Skye with Flora MacDonald?

5 Who betrayed William Wallace to the English in 1305?

6 What was the name of the Archbishop of St Andrews, murdered by the Covenanters in 1678?

7 Who was the chief favourite of James III, hanged beneath Lauder bridge by nobles in 1482?

8 Where was Rob Roy born?

9 Who was 'Bobbin' Johnnie'?

10 Which Roman governor of Britain began an invasion of the north in AD 80?

11 How old was Mary Queen of Scots when she came to the throne?

12 What was the name of the Act passed in 1703 which stated that Scotland would not accept a Hanoverian monarch without guarantees protecting both their religion and their trade?

13 Who led the English forces at Culloden?

14 What was the name of the ironworks specialising in military munitions founded near Falkirk in the mid-18th century?

15 Who left the Liberals to found the Scottish Socialist Party in 1888?

ANSWERS

1. James V 2. Malcolm IV 3. General Leslie 4. Betty Burke, Flora's maid 5. Sir John Menteith 6. James Sharp 7. Cochrane 8. Glengyle 9. The Earl of Mar, leader of the Jacobites after the death of Queen Anne in 1714 10. Agricola 11. One week 12. The Act of Security 13. The Duke of Cumberland 14. The Carron Ironworks 15. Keir Hardie

TRIVIA

1 What colour is the sand at Gruinard Bay?

2 What are 'Glasgow magistrates'?

3 How many varieties of Scottish granite went to make the pulpit of Crathie church on Deeside?

4 What colour is the Scottish primrose?

5 How high is the island of Ailsa Craig?

6 The Black Wood of Rannock is a remnant of what?

7 Where on the mainland of Scotland does the Scottish primrose, *Primula scotica*, grow?

8 What does the Gaelic word 'Bun' mean?

9 Who is Nickie-ben?

10 What is the only habitat of the field mouse *Apodemus sylvaticus butei*?

11 A 'burnewin' pursues what type of trade?

12 What is, or was, the Arran brown?

13 What is an 'oe'?

14 What is a clarsach?

15 The mines around Wanlockhead once produced which minerals?

ANSWERS

1. Pink 2. Loch Fyne herrings 3. 18 4. purple-red 5. 1,110 ft/335 m 6. The Caledonian Forest 7. Northern coasts 8. foot 9. The Devil 10. The island of Bute 11. Blacksmithing 12. A butterfly 13. A grandchild 14. A small Celtic harp 15. Zinc and lead

TV & ENTERTAINMENT

1   Who presented the first edition of 'Reporting Scotland'?

2   Which TV and radio performer writes plays under the name Frederic Mohr?

3   Which TV presenter is chairman of the Traverse Theatre, Edinburgh?

4   In which year was 'Songs of Scotland' first broadcast?

5   Sylvester McCoy appeared as a storyteller on which television programmes?

6   Pharic Maclaren produced which TV series, first shown in 1966?

7   In which television series did Ian McCaskill have a role, playing himself?

8   Who wrote the BBC radio series 'Down at the Mains'?

9   In which year did Fulton MacKay receive an OBE in the New Year's Honours List?

10 What was the television programme 'Forget About Me' originally called?

11 Who plays Archie Henderson in 'Doctor Finlay'?

12 From where were the first outside broadcasts made by the Gaelic service?

13 Who is associated with the role of Isabel Blair in 'Take the High Road'?

14 Harvey Keitel starred in which Scottish drama broadcast in 1988?

15 What was BBC Scotland's first live children's show?

ANSWERS

1. Mary Marquis 2. David McKail 3. Sheena McDonald 4. 1973 5. 'Harum Scarum' and 'Pass-the-Story' 6. 'The Vital Spark' 7. 'Birds of a Feather' 8. Gordon McCallum 9. 1984 10. 'Snow Queen' 11. Brian McCardie 12. Iona 13. Eileen McCallum 14. 'Down Where the Buffalo Go' 15. 'The United Shoelaces'

1   When does the season for stalking red deer end?

2   Who was Dave Mackay asked to mark in his 1957 international debut against Spain?

3   Where did speedboat racer John Cobbie die in 1952?

4   Who finished 4.5 seconds behind David Coulthard in the 1998 San Marino Grand Prix?

5   In which country was the Formula 2 race in which Jim Clark was killed in 1968?

6   Which football club plays in red and yellow striped shirts?

7   Which important UK golf tournament did Colin Montgomerie win in May 1998?

8   When was the last time that a Scot had won the same tournament?

9   What record did *Cable and Wireless Adventurer* achieve in July 1998?

10   How many miles did *Cable and Wireless Adventurer* travel in achieving this record?

11   Who captained *Cable and Wireless Adventurer* on the record-breaking voyage?

12   What is the name of St Johnstone's ground?

13   Peter Nicol won Scotland's first 1998 Commonwealth gold medal in which event?

14   With which club did Dave Mackay begin his football career?

15   Who scored Scotland's only goal in the 1986 World Cup Finals?

ANSWERS

1. 30 October 2. Alfredo Di Stefano 3. Loch Ness 4. Michael Schumacker 5. Germany (Hockenheim) 6. Partick Thistle 7. PGA 8. 1969 9. Fastest circumnavigation of the globe 10. 25,000 11. Jock Wishart 12. Muirton Park 13. Singles squash 14. Hearts 15. Gordon Strachan (against W Germany)

PEOPLE

1 At the time of the elections to the Scottish Parliament in 1999, what Cabinet post did Gavin Strang hold?

2 Who founded the Select Society in Glasgow in 1754?

3 Who was the 'heaven-taught ploughman'?

4 Who wrote *The Principles of Geology?*

5 What did 'shell-wives' do?

6 Which member of the Scottish Royal family died in Dundalk, Ireland, in 1318?

7 In which profession did Decimus Bruton excel?

8 The year 1778 saw the publication of *Flora Scotica*. Who wrote it?

9 What is the name of the poll-tax convict who leads the Scottish Socialist Party?

10 For which party did Sean Connery offer his support in the Scottosh parliamentary elections?

11 Which famous medieval historian was Abbot of Inchcolm Abbey?

12 What is distinctive about David Henderson of Conveth Mewis, Angus?

13 Who wrote *The Birds of Scotland* in 1806

14 Who carried a Saltire flag when he walked across the North Pole in 1996?

15 What fate befell 16th-century vagrant Johnnie Armstrong?

ANSWERS

1. Minster of Transport 2. Adam Smith 3. Robert Burns 4. Sir Charles Lyell 5. They were women who sold shellfish 6. Edward the Bruce 7. Architecture 8. Rev John Lightfoot 9. Tommy Sheridan 10. SNP 11. Walter Bower 12.The oldest man in Britain: 110 years old in May 1999 13. James Grahame 14. Jock Wishart 15. He led a group of vagrants to greet James V, who executed them thinking they were attacking the Royal party

1 Whose 'translations' of the poems of Ossian caused an uproar when they were first published in the late 18th century?

2 Whose first important book was his *Treatise On Human Nature*, written in the mid-1730s?

3 Who was the 'Ettrick Shepherd'?

4 Who wrote the trilogy of novels based on the 1745 Rising entitled 'The Jacobite Trilogy'?

5 Who wrote 'The Silver Darlings', regarded to be many as his best work?

6 Whose book of war memories is called 'Quartered Safe Out Here'?

7 On which South Sea island did Robert Louis Stevenson die?

8 Which of Alasdair Gray's novels was first published in hardback with fake reviews by the author himself?

9 Which English poet wrote the verse story for children 'Nessie, The Mannerless Monster'?

10 What are the Christian names of Dr Jekyll and Mr Hyde?

11 Whose first novel *Swing Hammer Swing* won the 1992 Whitbread Book of the Year award?

12 Who created the 16th-century Scottish mercenary Francis Crawford of Lymond and wrote a sequence of historical novels about him?

13 Which author became a Governor-General of Canada?

14 What did Sir Arthur Conan Doyle study at the University of Edinburgh?

15 Which children's writer created Katie Morag?

ANSWERS

1. James MacPherson 2. David Hume 3. James Hogg 4. D.K. Broster 5. Neil Miller Gunn 6. George MacDonald Fraser 7. Samoa 8. *Poor Things* 9. Ted Hughes 10. Henry and Edward 11. Jeff Torrington 12. Dorothy Dunnett 13. John Buchan 14. Medicine 15. Mairi Hedderwick

8

1 Whom was Rudolf Hess trying to meet when he flew to Scotland in 1941?

2 Which castle is the home of the Argyll and Southern Highlanders?

3 What does 'Inver' mean in a place name?

4 The name Gleneagles has nothing to do with eagles. what does it refer to instead?

5 What is a 'gaudsman'?

6 Which stately home has Scotland's largest private collection of furniture, china and silver?

7 The now-ruined Renaissance interior of which castle was called 'Lord Nithsdale's Daintie Fabrick'?

8 How many British regiments have Culloden among their battle honours?

9 Blairgowrie is a specialist centre for which area of horticulture?

10 What distinction does Cairnwall Pass hold?

11 Where is Old Leanack Farmhouse?

12 In which year were Aberdeen and Old Aberdeen united?

13 Which marque of car did Alexander Govan first design in 1899?

14 Which successful Hebridean textile association was formed in 1909?

15 Which of the two Uist islands has a predominantly Catholic population?

ANSWERS

1. The Duke of Hamilton 2. Stirling Castle 3. River mouth 4. A church ('eaglais' in Gaelic)
5. A ploughman 6. Drumlanrig Castle 7. Caerlaverock Castle 8. None 9. Soft fruit
10. Britain's highest main road (A93) summit 11. Culloden battle site 12. 1891 13. Argyll
14. Harris Tweed Association 15. South Uist

PLACES

1. Pollok is a Westminster constituency in which city?

2. Stirling is on the same line of longitude as which other British city?

3. The Fossil Forest in Victoria Park, Glasgow, has tree trunks that are how old?

4. How many miles wide is Scotland at its widest?

5. How much of a dip from peak to peak must there be for a mountain to qualifiy as a Munro?

6. Handa Island has always been famous for what?

7. Aberdeen lies between which two rivers?

8. Which is the largest of the Firth of Forth islands?

9. After whom is Grantown-on-Spey named?

10. Where would you find the peaks known as the Five Sisters?

11. How long is the River Tay?

12. Who is reputedly buried at Kilchoan Church?

13. What are the cliffs of Clo Mor made of?

14. The chief of which clan lay hidden in Cluny's Cave, near Newtonmore, for nine years to avoid capture after Culloden?

15. How long is the River Spey?

ANSWERS

1. Glasgow 2. Swansea 3. 230 million years 4. 154 miles 5. 500 ft/250 km 6. bird life 7. Dee and Don 8. Isle of May 9. Sir James Grant 10. Glen Shiel 11. 118 miles/190 km 12. Macbeth 13. sandstone 14. MacPherson 15. 110 miles/177 km

HISTORY

1 At the time of the elections to the Scottish Parliament, how many seats did the SNP hold in Westminster?

2 How did Alexander III die?

3 Calgacus led a Caledonain tribal army against the Romans in which battle?

4 In which year did the Scots defeat the English at Byland?

5 Where did Robert the Bruce assassinate John Comyn?

6 Which Scottish king was released from the Tower of London in 1357?

7 Whom did James V marry in 1537?

8 In which year was the Battle of Pinkie?

9 Where did John Knox preach his 1559 sermon against 'idolatry'?

10 Where was the Battle of Crab Stone fought in 1571?

11 Which battle of 1544 saw the MacDonnells and clan allies against the Frasers?

12 Where was the Battle of Justice Mills fought in 1644?

13 Which historical figure was held prisoner in Dunstaffnage Castle?

14 Tribes from which island gave Scotland its name?

15 In which decade did a group of artists called the Glasgow School emerge?

ANSWERS

1. Ten 2. He fell from cliffs at Kingshorn 3. Mons Graupius 4. 1322 5. Dumfries 6. David II 7. Madeleine, eldest daughter of the French king 8. 1547 9. St John's Kirk, Perth 10. Aberdeen 11. Battle of the Shirts 12. Aberdeen 13. Flora MacDonald 14. Ireland 15. 1880s

1 The McLean family from Renfrewshire played host to which uninvited guest in May 1941?

2 Who represents Hamilton South in the Westminster Parliament?

3 An Act of 1695 prohibited the removal of what from sand dunes?

4 What is *Cochlearia scotica*?

5 What is a howdie?

6 What does 'baggity' mean?

7 The beach at Tanera Beg is made of what?

8 Why is Bass Rock so called?

9 What is the natural haunt of the capercaillie?

10 What are 'haughlands'?

11 What is a 'tulchin'?

12 Can whisky make a person eemis?

13 What is the English name of Eilean a' Chleirich?

14 What is a custock?

15 What is a hallion?

ANSWERS

1. Rudolf Hess 2. George Robertson 3. Marram grass 4. Scottish scurvy grass 5. A midwife 6. Greedy 7. Coral sand 8. When its rock is struck with a hammer it sounds like a bell 9. Pine forest 10. alluvial meadows 11. a calfskin stuffed with straw to make a cow give milk 12. Yes - it means unsteady 13. Priest Island 14. A cabbage stem 15. A rogue

TV & ENTERTAINMENT

1 Which television presenter hosted 'Closer to Home' a documentary about American Scots?

2 What musical position did David McCallum's father hold?

3 What role did David McCallum play in 'The Man from U.N.C.L.E.'?

4 Who plays Rev Michael Ross in 'Take the High Road'?

5 Who played Eddie Clockerty in 'Tutti Frutti'?

6 Which television presenter once worked as fashion editor for the *Sunday Scot*?

7 Which versatile actor performed his one-man show 'Last Tango in Bangor' while at university in Wales?

8 Who played the title role in the film *Legend of the Werewolf*?

9 Who plays Effie Macinnes in 'Take the High Road'?

10 How was the film *The Pope Must Die* retitled for US distribution?

11 Who played Elizabeth Cunningham in 'Take the High Road' from 1980 to 1987?

12 Who played Lady Jane in 'Lovejoy'?

13 Who was Britain's youngest-ever daytime radio presenter?

14 Who played Piglet Ives in the film *The Great Escape*?

15 Which popular television star made her debut on Scottish Children's Hour, aged 12?

ANSWERS

1. Sheena McDonald 2. Leader of the Scottish Orchestra 3. Ilya Kuryakin 4. Gordon MacArthur 5. Richard Wilson 6. Carol Smillie 7. John Sessions 8. David Rintoul 9. Mary Riggans 10. *The Pope Must Diet* 11. Edith MacArthur 12. Phyllis Logan 13. Ross King 14. Angus Lennie 15. Eileen McCallum

SPORT

9

1 Who, in 1998, became the first Scot to win the British Open Squash Championship?

2 A captain of a team in which sport is known as the 'skip'?

3 Willie Woodburn, Sammy Cox, Ian McColl...who was the fourth member of Rangers' 'iron curtain' defence during the post-war years?

4 Who was a Scottish international in rugby and also won the Scottish Lawn Tennis Championships in 1879?

5 In which two sports did Eric Liddell compete internationally?

6 What was the name of the Rangers goalkeeper who was stretchered off with a head injury during the 1953 Scottish Cup Final replay against Aberdeen?

7 In which two sports did GPS Macpherson compete internationally?

8 In which year did Alan Tait play as a British Lion?

9 Which team, in the 1948-9 season, was the first to win the triple crown of the Championship, Scottish Cup and League Cup?

10 How many times has Scott Hastings been capped?

11 Which is Scotland's oldest rowing club?

12 Which rowing record do George P Parsonage and Peter Haining hold?

13 Which were the first World Cup Finals in which Scotland participated?

14 Who is Scotland's most capped stand-off?

15 Which race course, which closed in 1975, was Scotland's oldest?

ANSWERS

1. Chris Nicol 2. curling 3. George Young 4. Leslie Balfour-Melville 5. Rugby and athletics 6. George Niven 7. Rugby and long jump 8. 1997 9. Rangers 10. 66 11. St Andrews Boat Club, Edinburgh 12. Double-scull rowing the length of Loch Ness 13. Switzerland, 1954 14. Craig Chalmers 15. Lanark

PEOPLE

1 Who was Scotland's first Muslim MP?

2 Archibald the Grim, who died in 1400, was the third Earl of which clan?

3 Robert the Bruce died of which disease?

4 The Earls of Aberdeen live in which country house?

5 Which Scottish nurseryman published *Herbarium Britannicum* in 1804?

6 Who was known as the Wolf of Badenoch?

7 Whose death in 1457 marks the last item cited in the *Scotichronicon*?

8 What nationality is Dr Josef Venglos?

9 Which former member of Runrig folk/rock group was an ardent campaigner in the 1999 Scottish Parliamentary elections?

10 Which Scottish adventurer rowed across the Atlantic in 1997?

11 The Candida Casa was whose first Christian church?

12 Which renegade Labour MP stood as an Independent in the 1999 Scottish Parliamentary elections?

13 Who designed Heriot's Hospital, Edinburgh?

14 What type of organisation did Glasgow printer Robert Foulis try to establish in 1752?

15 Who was Scotland's most famous portrait painter in the early 1800s?

ANSWERS

1. Mohammed Sarwar 2. Douglas 3. Leprosy 4. Haddo House 5. George Don 6. The Earl of Buchan 7. James I 8. Slovak 9. Donnie Munro 10. Jock Wishart 11. Saint Ninian 12. Dennis Canavan 13. William Wallace 14. A Scottish Academy of Art 15. Sir Henry Raeburn

1 Which Gaelic poet, a close friend of Hugh MacDiarmid's, was seriously injured at the battle of El Alamein in World War II, and went on to receive the Queen's Gold Medal for poetry in 1990?

2 Who retold the story of Greyfriars Bobby, which has become a children's classic?

3 Which novelist, born in Singapore in 1938, is best known for his historical novels, particularly those set in ancient Rome?

4 Which novelist, chiefly famous as a parodist and satirist, was born in Cardross in Strathclyde in 1721 and died in Italy in 1771?

5 Who wrote *HMS Ulysses*?

6 Whose first two novels were *The Trick Is To Keep Breathing* and *Foreign Parts*?

7 Whose most famous book is *The Private Memoirs Of A Justified Sinner*?

8 Which of RM Ballantyne's books was William Golding's *Lord Of The Flies* loosely based on?

9 What is the name of Prince Charles's children's book?

10 Who was Dr Johnson's Edinburgh-born biographer?

11 Which crime writer created the detectives Lindsay Gordon, Kate Brannigan and Tony Hill?

12 Which conductor founded the Scottish Opera?

13 Which ancient historian recorded Rome's first invasion of what is now Scotland?

14 What type of people were 'Makars'?

15 Who described Kirkwall as 'dirty and mean'?

ANSWERS

1. Sorley MacLean 2. Eleanor Atkinson 3. Allan Massie 4. Tobias Smollett 5. Alistair McLean 6. Janice Galloway 7. James Hogg 8. *The Coral Island* 9. *The Old Man Of Lochnagar* 10. James Boswell 11. Val McDermid 12. Sir Alexander Gibson 13. Tacitus 14. Medieval poets 15. Sir Walter Scott

GENERAL KNOWLEDGE

1   The name of which Hebridean island capital translates as 'the king's harbor'?

2   The name of the Isle of Muck translates as what?

3   Kings from which three countries are buried on Iona?

4   How many members of the new Scottish Parliament have been elected from constituencies?

5   Where did an exhibition of the Dead Sea Scrolls open in May 1998?

6   In which month is the Skye provincial Gaelic Mod held?

7   What is Cadence Design Systems of California planning to develop at the Alba Centre?

8   In politics, what is the AMS?

9   How many Glasgow constituencies are there in the new Scottish Parliament?

10 How many Lothian constituencies are there in the new Scottish Parliament?

11 How many MSPs are elected through party lists?

12 The chief of which clan is known as Lochiel?

13 Who was appointed sheriff-deputy of Selkirkshire in 1799?

14 What was the Old Pretender's full name?

15 Which Scottish leader distinguished himself with the French Army at Oudenarde in 1708?

ANSWERS

1. Portree, Skye 2. Swine 3. Scotland, Ireland and Norway 4. 73 5. Kelvingrove Art Gallery, Glasgow 6. June 7. a new generation of microchip 8. Additional Member System (of voting) 9. Ten 10. Nine 11. 56 12. Cameron 13. Sir Walter Scott 14. James Francis Edward Stuart 15. The Old Pretender

PLACES

1 Dundee sends how many MPs to Westminster?

2 How is Fair Isle noted, in terms of natural history?

3 Where does the River Clyde rise?

4 What bird is associated with Bass Rock?

5 On which island would you find McLeod's Table?

6 On which island would you find the Dwarfie Stane?

7 What geographical distinction does Muckle Flugga hold?

8 Musselburgh stands near the site of which 16th-century battle?

9 What is the name of the dramatic gorge at Braemore?

10 Where is the Devorgilla Bridge ?

11 Who built the Dene Bridge, Edinburgh?

12 The Westminster constituency Moray is held by which member of the SNP?

13 On which island was George Orwell staying when he wrote *1984*?

14 Which bridge at Coldstream links Scotland and England?

15 Which river runs through Dumfries?

ANSWERS

1. Two 2. sightings of rare birds 3. The Southern Uplands, west of Moffat 4. gannet 5. Skye 6. Hoy 7. It is northernmost point in the British Isles 8. Pinkie 9. Corrieshalloch Gorge 10. Dumfries 11. Thomas Telford 12. Margaret Ewing 13. Jura 14. Tweed Bridge 15. Nith

1   Where would you find the prehistoric settlement of Skara Brae?

2   Inchgarvie fort was rebuilt in 1779 as a defence against which American naval commander?

3   Bishop Arnold began the construction of which church in 1161?

4   What peculiar privilege did Queen Victoria grant to the Duke of Atholl in 1844?

5   In which northern loch did German U-boats surrender to Allied naval forces in 1945?

6   Which federation of clans faced the Camerons at the Battle of North Inch?

7   Malcolm Cranmore did homage to whom at Abernethy?

8   When did Scotland adopt the Gregorian calendar?

9   Who was ruler of Scotland at the time of Cromwell's death?

10 Who in 1689 issued Letters of Fire and Sword against the MacDonalds?

11 Who was High Commissioner for Scotland under Charles II?

12 To which town in France did James II retire?

13 Whom did William III appoint Secretary of State for Scotland with the task of pacifying the Highlands?

14 Who was appointed Commander-in-Chief of Scotland after William III's accession?

15 Whose 1961 account of Culloden is the most widely respected historical interpretation?

ANSWERS

1. West Mainland, Orkney 2. John Paul Jones 3. St Andrews 4. Permission to retain a standing army 5. Loch Eriboll 6. Clan Chattan 7. William the Conqueror 8. 1600 9. General Monk 10. James II of England 11. The Duke of York, later James II (VII) 12. St-Germain 13. George Melville 14. General Hugh Mackay 15. John Prebble

1 What was a 'trental'?

2 For which site did Prince Albert pay £32,000 in 1832?

3 In which year were the modern Highland Games begun in Braemar?

4 Sir James Grant gave his name to which town?

5 What is the Dwarfie Stane?

6 Whose grandfather built the lighhthouse at Muckle Flugga in the Shetlands?

7 What was a 'targe'?

8 Which Scots financier founded the Bank of France?

9 When was yestreen?

10 Where is the Braw Lads Gathering?

11 The word 'tartan' derives from which language?

12 What is the great symphony music for bagpipes called?

13 What is a philabeg?

14 How was Forvie village in Aberdeenshire destroyed in the 1670s?

15 Where is the Gurd Nychburris Festival?

ANSWERS

1. A series of 30 masses said for the dead 2. Balmoral 3. 1832 4. Grantown-on-Spey 5. A 5000-year-old rock-cut tomb 6. Robert Louis Stevenson 7. A circular wooden shield covered in leather 8. John Law 9. Last night 10. Galashiels 11. French: from the word 'tiretaine', meaning a type of cloth 12. Pilbroch 13. A little wrap 14. The removal of marram grass from local sand dunes 15. Dumfries

TV & ENTERTAINMENT

1 Who played Doctor Who from 1987 to 1989?

2 Who played John Grey in two series of 'Trainer'?

3 Who played Rev Jonathan Green in TV's 'Cluedo'?

4 Who plays PC Reg Hollis in 'The Bill'?

5 Who played Joe Orton in the stage production of *The Orton Diaries*?

6 Who played Boswell in the television production 'Dialogue in the Dark'?

7 Who played Lawer Petello in 'Doon Castle'?

8 Which performer has acting credits for 'Doctor Who' and writing credits for 'Terry and June'?

9 Who playes Ruari Galbraith in 'Take the High Road'?

10 Which popular TV and radio presenter began his career as a warm-up man for BBC Scotland?

11 Who plays Dosser in 'Rab C Nesbitt'?

12 Who plays Mrs Mack in 'Take the High Road'?

13 Who played the barrister defending Kate Hughes in 'Emmerdale'?

14 Which fashion and travel presenter on television began her training at the Glasgow School of Art?

15 Which prolific actress presented two series of 'Gardener's Calendar'?

ANSWERS

1. Sylvester McCoy 2. David McCallum 3. Richard Wilson 4. Jeff Stewart 5. John Sessions 6. David Rintoul 7. Angus Lennie 8. John Kane 9. Charles Jamieson 10. Gordon Inglis 11. Russell Hunter 12. Gwyneth Guthrie 13. Sheila Grier 14. Muriel Gray 15. Hannah Gordon

1   In which two sports did Andy Goram compete internationally?

2   What was the year of the 'Wembley Wizards'?

3   In which year was St Andrews Boat Club, Edinburgh, founded?

4   Which sport derives from the ancient sport of camanachd?

5   Which other English club did Hughie Gallagher join when he left Newcastle in 1930?

6   Which team plays at Stark's Park?

7   Who was a Scottish rugby international and also British Amateur Golf Champion in 1895?

8   Alan Tait plays for which rugby league team?

9   How many times has Craig Chalmers been capped internationally?

10 Who was World Sculling Champion in 1993, 1994 and 1995?

11 Against which team did Scotland score their only point in the 1958 World Cup Finals in Sweden?

12 In which year was the first seven-a-side rugby tournament?

13 Within five, how many sportsmen have represented Scotland at both rugby and cricket?

14 In which two sports did JP Fisher compete internationally?

15 Name either of the cars that Jackie Stewart drove in winning his three world championships.

ANSWERS

1. Football and cricket 2. 1928 3. 1850 4. Shinty 5. Chelsea 6. Raith Rovers 7. Leslie Balfour-Melville 8. Widnes 9. 52 10. Peter Haining 11. Yugoslavia 12. 1883 13. 35 14. Rugby and basketball 15. Matra (1969) and Tyrrell (1971 and 1973)

PEOPLE

1 Which Cabinet Minister represents East Edinburgh and Musselburgh?

2 Which 17th-century Aberdeen merchant was known as 'Danzig WIllie' because of his trade links with Baltic ports?

3 Who was the last peer of the realm to be executed for treason?

4 Which famous Scottish geologist was knighted by Queen Victoria at Balmoral?

5 Who modified Robert Adam's original design for Edinburgh University?

6 Which 18th-century heroine was born at Milton, South Uist?

7 The MacCrimmons were hereditary pipers for which clan?

8 To which religious order did John Duns Scotus belong?

9 Which 18th-century road designer was born in Ayr?

10 How did the Hon Elsie Mackay die in 1929?

11 Which poet was born in Barrhead, Strathclyde, in 1857?

12 How did Glasgow merchant Thomas Lipton make his fortune?

13 Which pioneering surgeon was born in Bathgate, Lothian, in 1811?

14 Which explorer was born in Foulshiels, Borders, in 1771?

15 Name the lead singer of the pop group Simple Minds?

ANSWERS

1. Gavin Strang 2. William Forbes 3. Simon Fraser, the 11th Lord Lovat 4. Sir Charles Lyell 5. William Henry Playfair 6. Flora Macdonald 7. MacLeod 8. Franciscans 9. John Macadam 10. Flying a plane across the Atlantic 11. John Davidson 12. In the tea trade 13. Sir James Simpson 14. Mungo Park 15. Jim Kerr

1 'Fear not, till Birnam wood Do come to' - where?

2 What is the urlar, in pipe music?

3 Ruso Castle inspired Scott to write which novel?

4 Which novel did George Orwell write while staying on Jura?

5 In which Scott novel would you encounter Sir John de Walton?

6 Who wrote *A Counterblast to Tobacco*?

7 Which famous literary journal was founded in 1802 by Francis Jaffrey?

8 The Ossian tales were based on which Irish hero?

9 *An Inland Voyage,* written in 1878, was which famous writer's first book?

10 Who wrote *The Treatise of Human Nature?*

11 Who were the 'Castalian band'?

12 In which Scott novel would you encounter Francis Osbaldistone?

13 Who claimed to be 'half a Scot by birth and bred a whole one'?

14 Who wrote the Professor Challenger stories?

15 Where is the School of Scottish Studies located?

ANSWERS

1. Dunsinane, from *Macbeth* 2. The statement of melody 3. *Young Lochinvar* 4. *1984* 5. *Castle Dangerous* 6. James VI 7. *Edinburgh Review* 8. Oisin 9. Robert Louis Stevenson 10. David Hume 11. Poets in the court of James VI 12. (Rob Roy) 13. Lord Byron 14. Arthur Conan Doyle 15. Edinburgh

GENERAL KNOWLEDGE

1. What farming practice always took place at Martinmas in the Middle Ages?

2. Grime's Dyke is another name for which Roman Wall?

3. Agricola's Dere Street is often shown on maps as a branch of which other Roman road?

4. What is Dickman's Den, near Arbroath?

5. What, in medieval times, was a 'girnel'?

6. Where did Robert the Bruce allegedly witness the perserverance of the spider?

7. What is the traditional gathering place for crowds celebrating Hogmanay in Glasgow?

8. Which company owned the site being cleared to build the new Scottish Parliament?

9. What, in medieval times, was a 'mart'?

10. Which island, used as a missile tracking station since the 1950s, did British troops finally leave in 1998?

11. Who convened a Parliament at Holyrood Abbey in February 1334?

12. The former Scottish Parliament House, used between 1640 and 1707, is now part of which buildings?

13. Who owned a house on the site of the new Scottish Parliament and used it as a base for opposition to the Act of Union in 1707?

14. Who, in 1998, became the first woman minister to take charge of a Church of Scotland cathedral?

15. Which cathedral will be her responsiblity?

ANSWERS

1. Slaughtering of livestock 2. The Antonine Wall 3. Watling Street 4. A red sandstone cliff 5. A meal chest 6. In a cave on Arran 7. George Square 8. Scottish and Newcastle plc 9. A slaughtered animal 10. St Kilda 11. Edward Balliol 12. The High Courts 13. Andrew Fletcher 14. Rev Susan Brown 15. Dornoch Cathedral

1   Where is Telford's Spey Bridge?

2   On which island would you find Loch Snizort?

3   Alexandria, Strathclyde, was once the production centre for which make of car?

4   On which island is Maeshowe Chambered Cairn?

5   On which island is Fort Charlotte?

6   Which famous historical figure lived at St Bride, Douglas, Lanarkshire?

7   Which horror story was composed while the author strolled along the shores of Cruden Bay?

8   The summit of Knock, near Alves in the Highlands, was supposedly the site of which famous meeting?

9   Which Orkney port received Hudson's Bay Company ships on their way to Canada?

10 Which island capital's name translates from the Norse 'Kirk Vagr', meaning 'Church by the bay'?

11 Who built the highly decorated chapel at Lamb Holm, Orkney?

12 On which island is the Bay of Skaill?

13 Floors Castle lies just outside which town?

14 Which 15th-century fortress lies on an island below the Forth Bridge?

15 Glamis Castle is thought to have been a Royal residence as far back as which century?

ANSWERS

1. Craigellachie 2. Skye 3. Argyll 4. West Mainland, Orkney 5. Lerwick 6. Sir James Douglas, 'Black Douglas' 7. *Dracula* 8. Macbeth and the Weird Sisters 9. Stromness 10. Kirkwall 11. Italian POWs in the Second World War 12. West Mainland, Orkney 13. Kelso 14. Inchgarvie 15. 11th century

HISTORY

1 Which people were first mentioned in two Latin sources of AD297?

2 Which group of people attacked Scotland from their kingdom Deira in what is now Yorkshire?

3 In what year did Saint Columba die?

4 The Briton tribal King Coel Hen was the basis of which nursery rhyme character?

5 Who sacked Dumbarton in AD870?

6 Who were the Culdees?

7 Sigurd the Stout married which Scotish king's daughter?

8 The 10th-century Bishop of Cellach held what other ecclesiastical title?

9 What function did a 'derbfine' perform in ancient Gaelic society?

10 Which centre became Scotland's religious capital after Iona was sacked repeatedly by Danes?

11 In what year did the Battle of the Standard take place in Northallerton?

12 What, in relation to Scotland, did Pope John XXII formally authorise in 1329?

13 What was the title of the king's chief military officer in the 12th century?

14 What was Bagimont's Roll?

15 Who was the last king of Strathclyde?

ANSWERS

1. The Picts 2. Angles 3. 597 4. Old King Cole 5. Danes from Ireland 6. Medieval clergy who lived in communities 7. Malcolm II 8. Bishop of All Scotland, or Bishop of Alban 9. it was a group of men of royal blood who elected a new king 10. Dunkeld 11. 1138 12. Unction and coronation of Scottish monarchs 13. Constable 14. An assessment of the clergy's wealth for Vatican tithe purposes 15. Owen-the-Bald

1 Who represents Glasgow Anniesland in the Westminster Parliament?

2 What is the seann traibhas?

3 What were known as 'peesers'?

4 On which day of the week are the Balmoral Gardens closed to the public because the Royal Family might be in residence?

5 What is the Bullers of Buchan?

6 How was St Mary's Church, Glasgow, destroyed in 1793?

7 How long must whisky mature before it can be sold?

8 Who lives at Yesnaby Castle, Orkney?

9 What is unusual about the chapel at Lamb Holm, Orkney?

10 It is said that the test of a good Shetland garment is to be able to draw it through what?

11 In which group of islands is Papa Stour?

12 What was the 'ting' of Tingwall?

13 St. Adamnan wrote a famous biography of whom?

14 What did William de Somerville supposedly kill in Linton, near Kelso, in 1124?

15 What is Mavis Grind?

ANSWERS

1. Donald Dewar 2. A Highland dance 3. Young pigeons bred for eating 4. Sunday 5. A 200-foot chasm in cliffs 6. Burnt by drunken members of the local Hell Fire Club 7. Three years 8. No one: it is a red sandstone tower 9. It was built by Italian POWs from Nissen huts 10. A wedding ring 11. Shetland 12. A Norse parliament 13. Saint Columba 14. A dragon 15. An isthmus on Mainland, Shetland

TV & ENTERTAINMENT

1   Who plays Bunnie McKinnon in 'Forget About Me'?

2   Which TV presenter worked on both 'Wemyss Bay' and 'Scottish Woman'?

3   Who played Nancy Muir in the TV mini-series *Ghosts of the Emperor*?

4   Which televison presenter has been associated with 'Breakout' and 'The Disney Club'?

5   Who played Mairi in 'The Shuter Falls'?

6   Ian Glen played Brendan in which African-based film?

7   Which former Goodie presented three series of 'Tell the Truth'?

8   Who created the role of Sheila Ramsay in 'Take the High Road'?

9   Who played Mellor in 'The Bill'?

10 Who played Willie Gillespie in 'Take the High Road'

11 Who played Jeremy in four series of 'Don't Wait Up'?

12 Which presenter of 'Daytime Live' was formerly an international-level water polo player?

13 Who had the title role in TV's 'Sutherland's Law'?

14 Who plays Margaret Meldrew in 'One Foot in the Grave'?

15 Which Dunfermline-born actor had the title role in the TV series 'Shine on Harvey Moon'?

ANSWERS

1   Which captain of the Royal and Ancient Golf Club also represented Scotland in cricket for 36 years between 1876 and 1910?

2   In which two sports has Alan Tait competed internationally?

3   How did Hughie Gallagher take his own life, the night before he was due in court to face a charge of ill-treatment to his daughter in 1957?

4   Who holds the single-scull record for rowing the length of Loch Ness?

5   What is Dunfermline's nickname?

6   What is the record attendance for a rugby international?

7   Which Celtic player was nicknamed 'Caesar'?

8   Which horse race, said to be the oldest in the world, dates from the time of William the Lion?

9   Is Hamilton a flat or jump race course?

10 What is the surname of the five brothers who played for Wigtownshire RFC in 1992?

11 For which team did Alex Young score 77 goals in 228 games between 1960 and 1967?

12 Which horse holds the record starting-price for a winner?

13 Which team won the championship in 1958 with 29 wins, 4 draws and 1 defeat, 13 points clear of Rangers, the runners-up?

14 Which Scottish horse won the 2,000 guineas in 1961?

15 In which year was the first complete Rugby International Championship (Scotland, England, Ireland and Wales)?

ANSWERS

1. Leslie Balfour-Melville 2. Rugby union and rugby league 3. He threw himself under a train 4. George D Parsonage 5. The Pars 6. 104,000 (Scotland v Wales in 1975) 7. Billy McNeill 8. The Lanark Silver Bell 9. Flat 10. Drysdale 11. Everton 12. Equinoctial (250-1 at Kelso) 13. Hearts 14. Rockavon 15. 1883

PEOPLE

1. Where would you find the Michael Bruce Cottage Museum?

2. Second Steward Poon of the Merchant Navy spent how many days alone on a raft after his ship the SS *Lomond* was torpedoed in 1943?

3. With a total of 262 in two minutes, in which event did Philip Atringstall set the record in 1989?

4. James Tylter achieved what 'first' in Edinburgh in 1784?

5. Within 5, how many Munros did John Broxap climb in 23 hours, 20 minutes in 1988?

6. Who was the last Covenanter martyr to be executed in Edinburgh?

7. In which year did the execution take place?

8. Where would you find the John Buchan Centre?

9. With a score of 111,201 points, which record did Christine and Elizabeth Gill, Jeanette MacGrath and Donald Ward set in 1987?

10. How many members are there in the Duke of Atholl's private army?

11. Within ten, how many Scots have won the Victoria Cross?

12. Which famous march did band-master Frederick J Ricketts compose in 1913?

13. Which famous Norwegian composer had an Aberdonian father?

14. Who wrote the musical composition 'Scottish Fantasies'?

15. Where would you find the Mary, Queen of Scots House?

ANSWERS

1. Kinnesswood 2. 133 days 3. Pancake tossing 4. First free-flight balloon ascent from British soil 5. 28 6. Rev John Renwick 7. 1688 8. Broughton, Borders 9. Highest cribbage score in 24 hours 10. 80 (including 25 pipers) 11. 108 12. 'Colonel Bogie March' 13. Edvard Grieg 14. Max Bruch 15. Jedburgh

MUSIC & LITERATURE

1 In which century is Scott's *Old Mortality* set?

2 Which author paid for the publishing of *Better Dead?*

3 What did Sir Thomas Urquhart of Cromarty propose forming in his 1653 book *Logopandecteision?*

4 How was the minstrel Roderick Morison better known?

5 Which author wrote of his experiences in the village of 'Drumlochty'?

6 Who wrote the 10,000-line poem *Doomesday* in 1614?

7 In which Scott novel would you encounter the young knight Aymer de Valence?

8 Which 18th-century writer served as a surgeon's mate in the West Indies?

9 Whose religious poetry was known collectively as the 'Dundee Psalms'?

10 *Baptist Lake,* written in 1894, was a light novel by whom?

11 Who wrote *Gallipoli Memories?*

12 Who wrote *Sentimental Tommie?*

13 What did *The Complaynt of Scotland,* written in 1549, describe?

14 Whose autobiography is entitled *The Atom of Delight?*

15 Who wrote *A Voyage to Arcturus?*

ANSWERS

1. 17th 2. J M Barrie 3. A universal language 4. The Blind Harpist 5. Ian Maclaren 6. Sir William Alexander 7. *Castle Dangerous* 8. Tobias Smollett 9. Robert Wedderburn 10. John Davidson 11. Compton Mackenzie 12. J M Barrie 13. Tales, dances and songs of shepherds 14. Neil M. Gunn 15. David Lindsay

93

GENERAL KNOWLEDGE

1 Which brewer once owned the land on which the new Scottish Parliament will stand?

2 In a good year how many skiers can the Cairngorms resort expect to have?

3 A total ban on what came into force on February 1, 1998?

4 What was unusual about the Balmoral Highland Challenge in April 1998?

5 Who is the famous mother of Bonnie, born in April 1998?

6 What was unusual about the British Army's 21-gun salute to honour the Queen's Birthday in April 1998?

7 Who is the SNP spokesperson for arts and culture?

8 Which US President is commemorated with a statue in Edinburgh's Old Carlton Cemetery?

9 What world distinction does this monument claim?

10 Within ten, how many golf courses are there in Scotland?

11 Which is the world's best-selling brand of whisky?

12 Which city has more booksellers per head of population than any other in the UK?

13 The Sika deer was introduced to Scotland from which country?

14 Hirta is the main island in which uninhabited group of islands?

15 Near which fishing port is the curious rock formation known as the Pint Stoup?

ANSWERS

1. William Younger 2. 200,000 3. Handguns 4. It was the first televised event from the grounds of Balmoral Castle 5. Dolly, the first cloned sheep 6. It was fired by female soldiers 7. Anne Lorne Gilles 8. Abraham Lincoln 9. The first statue of an American President outside the USA 10. 450 11. Johnny Walker Red 12. Edinburgh 13. Japan 14. St Kilda 15. Arbroath.

PLACES

1 On which island is Scalloway Castle?

2 From which house did the Earl of Mar call out the clans for the 1715 Jacobite Rising?

3 In which castle is the Room of the Nine Nobles?

4 On which river are the Falls of Rogie?

5 The shifting sandbank of Gizzen Briggs lies at the mouth of which forth?

6 Displaced 19th-century crofters founded the community of New Kildonan in which country?

7 The House of Tongue was formerly the seat of the chiefs of which clan?

8 Britain's highest waterfall lies beyond the head of which loch?

9 Which town in the north-west was founded by the British Fisheries Society?

10 Where would you find the Auld Brig o' Doon?

11 Along which famous road is the Glenfinnan Monument?

12 On which island is Castleby?

13 What is the tallest mountain on Lewis?

14 The name of which Hebridean island translates as 'the mountain of the fords'?

15 On which island are the Braighe Sands?

ANSWERS

1. Mainland, Shetland 2. Invercauld House 3. Crathes Castle 4. Blackwater 5. Dornoch 6. Canada 7. Mackay 8. Loch Glencoul 9. Ullapool 10. Aberdeen 11. Road to the Isles 12. Barra 13. Clisham 14. Benbecula 15. Lewis

HISTORY

1 The 10th-century Hebridean King Ketil Flatnose came from where?

2 Thorfiinn the Mighty was the grandson of which Scottish king?

3 Which were the Burghs represented in the medieval Court of the Four Burghs?

4 Yolande de Dreux was the widow of which Scottish king?

5 In which year did Scotland conclude the first formal treaty of the 'Auld Alliance'?

6 What were the Ragman Rolls?

7 Which Roman wall, built between AD138 and 143, stretched from Bo'ness west to Bowling?

8 In what year was the Stone of Destity recovered after its 'theft' from Westminster Abbey?

9 What did the famous Highland freebooter James Macpherson do on his way to the gallows in 1701?

10 Who were known by the Scots as the 'White Gentiles' in the 10th-century?

11 Which kings signed the Treaty of Corbeuil in 1326?

12 What was the northernmost Roman penetration in Scotland?

13 James Watt was commissioned to report on the feasibility of which engineering project in 1773?

14 Where was James III fatally stabbed?

15 Who were known by the Scots as the 'Black Gentiles' in the 10th-century?

ANSWERS

TRIVIA

1 Where is the Sneug?

2 What is Fanzie Girt?

3 What is Am Fear Lath Mor?

4 What, in the Orkneys, is a trow?

5 What was described as 'the garb of sedition'?

6 Moscow lies 12 miles south of which city?

7 What did the 17th-century book *The Secret Commonwealth*, by Rev Robert Kirk, describe?

8 Which manor house was christened 'Conundrum Castle' by its owner?

9 Berwick is still technically at war with which European power?

10 How is Anstruther pronounced?

11 The name of which weapon derives from the Gaelic for 'big sword'?

12 Which castle is said to be the most haunted in Scotland?

13 Which was the last British castle to be besieged?

14 Who is the only British subject permitted to retain a private standing army?

15 What is the maximum number of passengers carried by the 'Royal Scotsman' luxury train in the Highlands?

ANSWERS

1. Mainland, Shetland 2. Ruins of a stone wall that divided Fetlar, Shetland 3. The 'Big Grey Man' who haunts the Cairngorms 4. An ugly dwarf 5. The kilt in the 18th century 6. It is a hamlet near Glasgow 7. Fairies 8. Sir Walter Scott's nickname for Abbotsford 9. Russia: dating from the end of the Crimean War 10. 'Ainster' 11. Claymore 12. Glamis 13. Blair Castle, in 1746 14. The Duke of Atholl 15. 32.

TV & ENTERTAINMENT

1 Who played Birdie Bowers in 'The Last Place on Earth'?

2 In which year did Ian McCaskill begin weather forecasting for the BBC?

3 In which film about the *Titanic* did David McCallum have a large role?

4 Which Scottish actor's autobiography is subtitled *A Life Beyond the Grave?*

5 Which of John Sessions' films is unlikely ever to be shown at the Vatican?

6 Who had the title role in the radio production of 'Mary Queen of Scots'?

7 Who played the nurse Sandra Maghie in 'Brookside'?

8 Who presented the television series 'Art is Dead...Long Live TV'?

9 Who provided the voice for Hyzenthlay in the film *Watership Down?*

10 Who played Dr Claire Wainwright in 'Casualty'?

11 Who played Frankie in the mini-series 'Frankie's House'?

12 Which TV presenter and comedian has a song-writing credit for 'Make a Daft Noise for Christmas'?

13 Who played Thelma in 'The Likely Lads' and 'What Ever Happened to the Likely Lads'?

14 Who created the role of Morag Stewart in 'Take the High Road'?

15 Which versatile comic actor has appeared in stage productions of *The Cherry Orchard* and *As You Like It* as well as creating one of Scotland's most notorious comic heroes?

ANSWERS

1. Sylvester McCoy 2. 1978 3. *A Night to Remember* 4. Richard Wilson 5. *The Pope Must Die* 6. Gwyneth Guthrie 7. Sheila Grier 8. Muriel Gray 9. Hannah Gordon 10. Stella Gonet 11. Ian Glen 12. Graeme Garden 13. Brigit Forsyth 14. Jeannie Fisher 15. Gregor Fisher

SPORT

1   Which was the first rugby international to be televised?

2   By what score did Scotland beat New Zealand in the 1982 World Cup finals in Spain?

3   Which was Billy McNeill's first club as manager?

4   Which rugby club holds the record for most wins in Division 1?

5   Is Ayr a flat or jump race course?

6   Which sprinter ran the 100 metres in 21.7 seconds when aged 92?

7   Which club did Kenny Dalglish support as a schoolboy?

8   In which infamous match did Billy McNeill make his international debut?

9   In which year was Jock Stein appointed Celtic manager?

10   Which prominent Scottish sprinter beat a pony and trotting-car over 100 metres?

11   Who scored four tries against France and then four against Wales in 1925?

12   How many times was the Scottish League won by a team other than Rangers or Celtic between 1904 and the Second World War?

13   Which rugby player is known as Del Boy?

14   Which is the oldest professional sprint competition?

15   Who scored the most number of tries in a rugby international?

ANSWERS

1. England v Scotland in 1938 2. 5-2 3. Aberdeen 4. Hawick (10 between 1973 and 1986) 5. Both 6. Duncan McLean in 1977 7. Rangers 8. The 9-3 defeat against England at Wembley in 1961 9. 1965 10. George McNeill 11. Ian Smith 12. Once - Motherwell in 1931-32 13. Damien Cronin 14. The *Eric Liddell Memorial* New Year Sprint 15. George Lindsay (five against Wales in 1887)

PEOPLE

1   Where would you find the John Muir House?

2   What was the name of the 45-strong family executed for cannibalism during the reign of James VI?

3   Which French composer of the early 20th century had a Scots mother and was said to have been conceived when his parents were on honeymoon in the Highlands?

4   Why were gypsies Moyses, David, Robert and John Fa executed in 1611?

5   Where would you find the McDouall Stuart Museum?

6   After a visit to Scotland in 1618, which English poet was sentenced to having his nose cut off for making fun of the Scots?

7   Who was the last person to be hanged in Scotland?

8   Where did this execution take place?

9   Who created the world's first Panorama, in Edinburgh (1784)?

10 Where would you find the Giant Macaskill Museum?

11 What record did Angus Macaskill (b. 1823) achieve?

12 Which Scot was instrumental in the development of motion pictures?

13 Which Scot was scenic director of MGM Studios from 1939 to 1964?

14 A film of which Scottish writer's work was the first horror movie to be made?

15 Who is the only Scot to have been twice condemned, twice forfeited his estates, and twice pardoned and restored?

ANSWERS

1. Dunbar 2. Sawney Bean 3. Erik Satie 4. For remaining in the Kingdom 5. Dysart 6. Ben Jonson 7. Henry John Burnett, in 1963 8. 9. Robert Barker 10. Dunvegan, Skye 11. He was the tallest non-pathological giant (7 feet, 9 inches/2m 36cm) 12. David Brewster 13. George Gibson 14. Robert Louis Stevenson *Dr Jekyll and Mr Hyde* 15. Captain Simon Fraser of Beaufort

MUSIC & LITERATURE

1 What was Alistair MacLean's first published novel?

2 *Or, tis Sixty Years Since* is the subtitle to which famous novel?

3 Why did writer Alexander Montgomerie fall from favour in the Stuart court in 1597?

4 Who wrote *Ripeness is All?*

5 Who wrote *The Tea Table Mystery?*

6 Who compiled a 1924 anthology of Scots poetry entitled *The Northern Muse?*

7 Who wrote *Scottish Novel*, published in 1958?

8 Which military hero wrote the love poem 'My Dear Only Love'?

9 Who created the character Edie Ochiltree?

10 Dot Allen's novels take place in which city?

11 Who wrote the 1954 novel *Ben Nevis Goes East?*

12 Who wrote *The Private Memoirs and Confessions of a Justified Sinner?*

13 Who wrote the 1934 novel *Butcher's Broom?*

14 *Lost Country* is a collection of which poet's work?

15 In which Scott novel would you encounter Diana Vernon?

ANSWERS

1. *HMS Ulysses* 2. *Waverley* 3. He was implicated in a Catholic plot 4. Eric Linklater 5. Allan Ramsay 6. John Buchan 7. Tom Macdonald 8. The Marquis of Montrose 9. Sir Walter Scott 10. Glasgow 11. Compton Mackenzie 12. James Hogg 13. Neil M Gunn 14. Marion Angus 15. Rob Roy

GENERAL KNOWLEDGE

1 Which Scottish leader distinguished himself with the French army at Malplaquet in 1709?

2 How was Arbroath known in Scott's novel *The Antiquary?*

3 In which year did the last of Scotland's lighthouses become automated?

4 Which Internet service provider is owned by Scottish Power?

5 Which trio of beautiful women is owned jointly by the National Gallery of Scotland and the Victoria and Albert Museum?

6 How did US Senator Trent Lott promote Scottish interests in the United States in April 1998?

7 Do reindeer live in the wild in Scotland?

8 Which are the three three-letter place names in Scotland?

9 What is unusual about Strathisla in Keith?

10 How wide is Loch Lomond at its widest?

11 Which is Scotland's oldest inhabited castle?

12 On which island is this castle?

13 Which was the largest ship ever to be built in Scotland?

14 Within 500 square miles/1300 square kms, how large is Scotland?

15 How old was James IV when he came to the throne?

ANSWERS

1. The Old Pretender 2. Fairport 3. 1998 4. Demon 5. 'The Three Graces' 6. By promoting the bill to make 6 April National Tartan Day in the United States 7. Yes, in the Highlands 8. Oa, Ae and Bu 9. The oldest malt whisky distillery in Scotland 10. 5 miles/8 km 11. Dunvegan Castle 12. Skye 13. The QE2 14. 30,411 square miles/78,764 square kms 15. 15

PLACES

1 On which island is the Ring of Brodger?

2 The Heisker Islands lie just west of which Hebridean island?

3 The A868 runs through which island?

4 The Paps are a feature on which island?

5 Where would you find the Cowal Hills?

6 On which island was Flora Macdonald born?

7 Which Hebridean island capital has a name that translates as 'the well of Mary'?

8 Where would you find the Gardens of Kiloran?

9 Where would you find the 'Rents'?

10 Fionnphort is connected by ferry to which island?

11 The A888 forms a 14-mile loop around which island?

12 On which Hebridean island would you find the Ardtun Leaf Beds?

13 The small island of Erraid, near Iona, was the setting for part of which famous novel?

14 Which island is often described as 'Scotland in miniature'?

15 On which island is Kismul Castle?

ANSWERS

1. West Mainland, Orkney 2. North Uist 3. Lewis 4. Jura 5. Bute 6. South Uist 7. Tobermory, Mull 8. Colonsay 9. Arran 10. Iona 11. Barra 12. Mull 13. *Kidnapped* 14. Arran 15. Barra

HISTORY

1 Who won the Battle of Carham in 1018 to extend his territory south to the Tweed?

2 In which year did the Caledonian Canal open?

3 Which 1679 battle in Strathclyde resulted in a serious loss for the Covenanters?

4 An Islay Parliament met at which village between 1718 and 1843?

5 What did the General Assembly propose at Saint Columba parish church, Burntisland, in 1601?

6 Which loch lies nearest the site of the Glencoe Massacre?

7 Which North European trading alliance included Banff?

8 Which Prince of Wales bought the Birkhall Estate?

9 Where was the famous Ferry Disaster of 1809?

10 In which year did James III die?

11 Margaret the Maid of Norway succeeded which Scottish king?

12 Where did the Maid of Norway die in 1290 on her way to Scotland?

13 Where was the Stone of Destiny recovered after its 'theft' from Westminster Abbey?

14 The defeat of which Saxon king in the 10th-century led to the adoption of the Saint Andrew's Cross by the Scots?

15 Where was 'Peat' Einar Earl between 891 and 894?

ANSWERS

TRIVIA

1 Why was an iron suspension bridge built across the Dee downstream from Balmoral in 1924?

2 In which year did Queen Victoria first attend the Highland Games?

3 'Do Not vaiken sleiping Dogs' is which family's motto?

4 What is a doocot?

5 What were said to come in three types in Glen Urquhart: black, speckled and white?

6 How fast does a salmon travel when it leaps?

7 What record does Eas-coul-Aulin hold?

8 After visiting where in 1765 did Thomas Gray write 'there are certain scenes that would drive an atheist into belief'?

9 Who was the legendary Damh Mor?

10 The Sixth Fusk of what died in 1839, having reputedly gambled away £4 million and fathered 398 illegitimate children?

11 What was a 'howf'?

12 The riderless horse of which slain clan chief swam home to bring news of defeat at Culloden?

13 Which Biblical figure, according to folklore, was born in Fortingall?

14 What distinction does Tomintoul hold?

15 Banff was once a member of which North Sea trading partnership?

ANSWERS

1. For salmon fishermen 2. 1848 3. Forbes 4. A dovecote 5. devils 6. 20 miles per hour/ 32 Km/h 7. The highest waterfall in Britain 8. Skye 9. A stag that lived 200 years 10. Argyll 11. A cellar for storing oysters 12. Lachlan MacLachlan 13. Pontius Pilate 14. The highest village in the Highlands 15. The Hanseatic League

TV & ENTERTAINMENT

1   Who played Richard Hannay in a recent TV production of *The Thrity-nine Steps*?

2   Who played Andy O'Brien in 'Eastenders'?

3   Who had the title role in TV's 'Charles Endell Esquire'?

4   Who played Catherine of Aragon in 'The Six Wives of Henry VIII'?

5   Which Dundee-born actor won the Laurence Olivier Award for Best Actor in 1985 and 1989?

6   Who hosted the TV game show 'Small Talk'?

7   To which trade was Billy Connolly apprenticed?

8   Which Glasgow-born TV presenter was the first announcer heard on Channel Four?

9   Which 'Top of the Pops' presenter once wrote scripts for 'Spitting Image'?

10   Who played Sadie McDonald in 'Take the High Road'?

11   Who played Danny McGlone in 'Tutti Frutti'?

12   Which touring theatrical company, with a numbered name, aims to present drama to working-class audiences?

13   Who played PC Jock Weir in 'Z-Cars'?

14   Who starred in the popular West End shows 'On the Brighter Side' and 'Phil the Fluter'?

15   Who played Costas Caldes in the film *Shirley Valentine*?

ANSWERS

1. David Rintoul 2. Ross Davidson 3. Iain Cuthbertson 4. Annette Crosbie 5. Brian Cox 6. Ronnie Corbett 7. Shipyard welding 8. Paul Coia 9. Nicky Campbell 10. Doreen Cameron 11. Robbie Coltrane 12. 7:84 13. Joseph Brady 14. Stanley Baxter 15. Tom Conti

SPORT

1   Is Edinburgh a flat or jump race course?

2   Who won the first Scottish League Cup Final?

3   How many League goals did Danny McGrain score for Celtic during his 20 years with them?

4   In which year did Yvonne Murray win the gold in the European Championship 3000 metres?

5   Which rugby player is known as the White Shark?

6   In which season was the Scottish League Cup first played for?

7   Who holds the UK women's record for the 10,000 metres?

8   Who took gold in the men's 800 metres at the 1989 Europa Cup?

9   What is Ally McCoist's middle name?

10 Which sport is presided over by the Camanachd Association?

11 To which club was Danny McGrain appointed manager in 1992?

12 Which is the world's oldest continuously run foot race?

13 Which sprinter had a career that spanned more than 73 years?

14 How many times did the 5th Lord Roseberry win the Derby as a trainer?

15 Who holds the record for most points scored for Scotland in a rugby international?

ANSWERS

1. Both 2. Rangers, beating Aberdeen 4-0 3. five 4. 1990 5. John Jeffrey 6. 1946-7 7. Liz McColgan 8. Tom McKean 9. Murdoch 10. Shinty 11. Arbroath 12. The Carnwath Red Hose Race (1507) 13. Duncan McLean 14. Three times 15. Gavin Hastings (44 against Ivory Coast in 1995)

PEOPLE

1 Which brothel-keeper was hanged in front of 20,000 people in Edinburgh in 1823 for stabbing a solicitor's clerk?

2 Who was the New York murderer of eight people, hanged at Barlinnie Prison in 1958?

3 Which title did the MacDonalds forfeit to the Scottish Crown in 1493?

4 Who built Doune Castle?

5 Who was the first Commander of the US Navy?

6 Which heroine of an 18th-century ballad lived in Maxwelton House?

7 Which saint built a church at Whithorn at the end of the fifth century?

8 Which is the only Laurel and Hardy film to concern Scotland?

9 Who entertained Mary, Queen of Scots at Earlshall Castle, which he built in 1546?

10 Which cardinal's murdered body was hung from St Andrews Castle in 1546 as a warning against the 'sins of Catholicism'?

11 Which Scot became the first person to cross Australia from north to south, in 1862?

12 Which Scot commanded the highest fee for a comedian in a silent film?

13 Which king built the royal palace at Stirling Castle?

14 Who was Diogenes Teufelsdrokh?

15 Where would you find the Carlyle Birthplace?

ANSWERS

1. Mary McKinnon 2. Peter Manuel 3. Lordship of the Isles 4. Robert Stewart, Duke of Albany 5. John Paul Jones from Arbigland 6. Annie Laurie 7. Saint Ninian 8. *Bonnie Scotland, 1935* 9. Sir William Bruce 10. Cardinal Beaton 11. John McDouall Stuart 12. Harry Lauder (£10,000 in 1927) 13. James V 14. Thomas Carlyle (fictitious name for himself) 15. Ecclefechan

108

MUSIC & LITERATURE

1 Why would a musician 'tyrle'?

2 In which Scott novel would you encounter Herries of Birrenswork?

3 Whose ten-volume *History of Scotland* was published in Rome, and in Latin, in 1578?

4 What does 'jinkin' mean in Burns's poetry?

5 Which king did George Buchanan tutor?

6 What would a Lallans poem about 'nowt' concern?

7 *Chorus of the Newly Dead* is a collection of whose poems?

8 In which year did John Knox's *First Blast of the Trumpet Against the Monstrous Regiment of Women* appear?

9 In which field did 18th-century writer Robert Ferguson excel?

10 What does 'couthie' mean in Burns's poetry?

11 In which year was Robert Louis Stevenson's *Doctor Jekyl and Mr Hyde* published?

12 Who wrote the 1936 novel *No Mean City*, set in Glasgow?

13 Who wrote the novel *Grey Granite*?

14 Which king wrote *Daemonologue* as proof of the existence of witchcraft?

15 Who wrote the love poem *Under the Eildon Tree*?

ANSWERS

1. to touch strings 2. *Redgauntlet* 3. Bishop John Leslie 4. Dodging 5. James VI 6. Cattle 7. Edwin Muir 8. 1558 9. Poetry 10. Friendly 11. 1886 12. Alexander MacArthur 13. Lewis Grassic Gibbon 14. James VI 15. William Soutar

GENERAL KNOWLEDGE

1 How long is Loch Lomond?

2 Which is Scotland's largest malt whisky distillery?

3 Why does the Scottish flag fly perpetually in Athelstaneford churchyard?

4 Which famous resident, who died in 1795, is buried in Auchinleck churchyard?

5 The Glen Udalainn hydro-electric plant operates near which Highland village?

6 The Ballachulish Ferry crosses which loch?

7 Sguirr Dhearg and Sguirr Dhounill are collectively known as what?

8 Knockdolian and Kirkhill castles were strongholds of which clan?

9 Three members of which clan were outlawed in 1533 for the murder of Sir John MacLaurin?

10 Which sea rock can be seen from Ballantrae?

11 Where are the Twa Brigs?

12 Which set of eight locks lifts the Caledonian Canal by 64 feet/20 metres?

13 Where is the permanent 'Forging of a Nation' exhibition?

14 Near which Borders town are the three-peaked Eildon Hills?

15 Which wood, famous from *Macbeth,* lies near Auldearn?

ANSWERS

1. 23 miles/37 km 2. Tomatin 3. It was adopted as a Scottish emblem there after a 10th-century victory over the Saxons 4. James Boswell 5. Auchtertyre 6. Leven 7. Ben Vair 8. Kennedy 9. McLaren 10. Ailsa Crag 11. Ayr 12. Neptune's Staircase 13. Bannockburn 14. Bemersyde 15. Hardmuir

1 The A865 links which three Hebridean islands?

2 Where would you find Lamlash?

3 On which island is the Eye Peninsula?

4 Edinburgh is named after which king?

5 Glasgow's name is a corruption of 'Glas Cau', meaning what?

6 Saint Serfs is the largest island in which loch?

7 Black Isle lies between which two firths?

8 On which island is Loch Corruisk?

9 A judge overruled a 1998 conservation protest about building a funicular railway where?

10 What is the name of the new microcomputing complex in Livingston?

11 Which company took over Prestwick International Airport in May 1998?

12 Where is Scotland's northernmost distillery?

13 What was the former name of Castle Douglas?

14 Which church has the tallest spire in Edinburgh?

15 On which island is Dun Carloway Broch?

ANSWERS

1. North Uist, Benbecula and South Uist 2. Arran 3. Lewis 4. Edwin of Northumbria 5. Green place 6. Loch Leven 7. Moray and Cromarty 8. Skye 9. The Cairngorms 10. Alba Centre 11. Stagecoach 12. Orkney; Highland Park 13. Carlingwark 14. Tolbooth Kirk 15. Lewis

HISTORY

1 What was Edward Balliol's relationship to King John of England?

2 Who spent the years 1334-41 in Chateau Gaillard, France?

3 An Act of 1312 established whom as Robert the Bruce's successor?

4 For how many years did David II reign?

5 Angus Og, an ally of Robert the Bruce, was the ancestor of which famous clan?

6 What were the *feu-ferme* charters?

7 Who landed at Kinghorn in 1332 as his first step in invading Scotland?

8 Which family was raised to the Peerage in 1647 as Earls of Dundonald?

9 Which Douglas chief took the heart of Robert I with him on the Crusades?

10 Which castle did Black Agnes, Countess of March, hold for five months against an English siege in 1338?

11 Which bridge, built over the Coldingham Road in the Lammermuir Hills in the late 18th century, spans 300 feet/91 metres and was also reckoned to be the highest bridge in the world upon completion?

12 Where were the Scottish Royal regalia taken for safekeeping when Cromwell occupied Scotland in 1650?

13 Which Scottish king married Joan, daughter of King John of England?

14 In which castle was Mary, Queen of Scots executed?

15 Which English king came as far north as Lochindorb, Moray, in 1336?

ANSWERS

1. He was John' son 2. David II 3. His brother Edward 4. 42 5. Donald 6. Annual payments made by the burghs to the king 7. Edward Balliol 8. Cochrane 9. Sir James 'the Good' 10. Dunbar 11. Pease Bridge 12. Dunnoter Castle 13. Alexander II 14. Fotheringay 15. Edward III

1 In which castle is the Plague supposedly kept in a magic bottle?

2 Near which town are the Clava Cairns?

3 What are the three Kings of Cullen?

4 The 'Aberdeen Maiden' was said to be the model for which French invention?

5 What, according to legend, was Jacob's Pillow?

6 What is a small loch called?

7 According to legend. which clan chief refused Noah's offer of hospitality because he had a boat of his own?

8 A princess from which country is said to be buried on Beinn na Caillich, Skye?

9 Boswell and Johnson were stranded for ten days on which island during their Highland Tour?

10 What are the 'Rents' on Arran?

11 What are 'pirns'?

12 The Kyle rail line links Kyle of Lochalsh with which town?

13 Who was the last king to be crowned at Scone?

14 Whithorn is said to be the birthplace of which saint?

15 Why did Brigitte Bardot fly to Edinburgh in her private jet in 1998?

ANSWERS

1. Castle Urquhart 2. Inverness 3. Coastal rocks 4. The guillotine 5. The Stone of Destiny 6. A lochan 7. MacNeill of Barra 8. Norway 9. Coll 10. Spectacular crevasses 11. Wooden bobbins 12. Inverness 13. James VI 14. Ninian 15. To save the dog Woofie from execution

TV & ENTERTAINMENT

1   What character does Richard Wilson play in 'One Foot in the Grave'?

2   Who played Boswell in the TV programme 'A Tour of the Wester Isles'?

3   Which versatile actor began his career as a dancer until talent-spotted by Vivivan Van Damm?

4   Which Scottish radio presenter has been associated with 'Take 5', 'Sportsbeat' and 'Fantasy Football'?

5   Who, also known for her roles in 'Brookside' and 'Emmerdale', presented 'The United Shoelaces' programme on television?

6   Who has appeared on 'The Tube', 'Acropolis Now' and 'The Media Show'?

7   Who played Beatrice Eliott in three series of 'The House of Eliott'?

8   Which TV actor/writer has compiled a book of 'very silly games'?

9   Which actor carried a successful London performance in *Rat in the Skull* to an equally praised Broadway run?

10   Who starred in the TV series 'Sorry'?

11   Who was Gerry Rafferty's partner in the folk-music duo The Humblebums?

12   Who presented the TV series 'Holy Spirits'?

13   Which actor appeared in the following films: *Eat the Rich, Let It Ride* and *Nuns on the Run?*

14   Name the host of the TV game show 'Win, Lose, Draw'.

15   In which year did Nicky Campbell join Radio 1?

ANSWERS

1. Victor Meldrew 2. John Sessions 3. Angus Lennie 4. Ross King 5. Sheila Grier 6. Muriel Gray 7. Stella Gonet 8. Graeme Garden 9. Brian Cox 10. Ronnie Corbett 11. Billy Connolly 12. Tom Conti 13. Robbie Coltrane 14. Paul Coia 15. 1987

1 How many times did the 5th Lord Roseberry win the 2,000 Guineas as a trainer?

2 Where is the *Eric Liddell Memorial* New Year Sprint held each year?

3 Is Kelso a flat or jump race course?

4 Which was Ally McCoist's first club?

5 Which Scottish woman was the 1990 World 10,000 metres champion?

6 Which record did Alfred Downer set in 1897?

7 From which English club did Rangers buy Ally McCoist in 1983?

8 Which marching song was inspired by a golfer whistling to a fellow golfer at Fort George golf course in 1913?

9 Which football club is nicknamed The Bairns?

10 Which team won the Scottish League Cup three times in the first eight seasons of the competition?

11 Where did Liz McColgan set her UK 10,000-metre record in 1991?

12 Which rugby player is known as Mighty Mouse?

13 Which club did Aberdeen beat in the 1983 European Cup-winners' Cup final?

14 How many times did trainer Tom Dawson win the Derby?

15 Who holds the record for most points scored for Scotland in an international rugby union career?

ANSWERS

1. Twice 2. Meadowbank 3. Jump 4. St Johnstone 5. Liz McColgan 6. World professional 400 metres 7. Sunderland 8. 'Colonel Bogie March' 9. Falkirk 10. East Fife 11. Tokyo 12. Ian McLaughlin 13. Real Madrid 14. Twice 15. Gavin Hastings (676 points in 61 games)

PEOPLE

1   Where would you find the Andrew Carnegie Birthplace Museum?

2   Where would you find the Carnegie Museum?

3   What was unusual about the 1842 trial of the Rosenbergs in Aberdeen?

4   Where would you find a museum devoted to the collections of 19th-century trader Adam Arbuthnot?

5   Which distillery was founded by William Grant in 1886?

6   Which clan is descended from one of the last Norse kings of Man and the North Isles?

7   Who sculpted the figure of the Highlander who appears on the Glenfinnan Monument?

8   Which saint reputedly admonished the Loch Ness monster in the sixth century?

9   Which clan cherishes the Black Chanter, which is said to have fallen from the heavens at the Battle of Inch?

10 In which year were the ten 'Glasgow Dynamiters' convicted of trying to blow up Canal Bridge at Possill and sentenced to penal servitude?

11 Which statesman made Fasque, near Laurencekirk, his country home from 1830 to 1851?

12 Which pair of 19th-century brothers founded a natural history museum in Forres?

13 Which planner of Dunrobin Castle's restoration was also the chief architect of the Houses of Parliament?

14 Which 17th-century soldier was known as the 'Black Colonel'?

15 Where would you find Hugh Miller's Cottage?

ANSWERS

1. Dunfermline 2. Inverurie 3. The only instance of a Scottish trial extending into Sunday morning 4. Peterhead 5. Glenfiddich 6. MacLeod 7. John Greenshields 8. Saint Columba 9. Macpherson 10. 1883 11. W E Gladstone 12. Alexander and Hugh Falconer 13. Sir Charles Barry 14. John Farquharson of Inverey 15. Cromarty

1 Whose retelling of the Irish Fenian tales became popular in 19th-century Europe?

2 In which city did Lord Byron go to school?

3 Which Scottish novel concerns the struggles between Cavaliers and Covenanters?

4 Under what pen-name are the works of J. Leslie Mitchell written?

5 Who was Sir Walter Scott's biographer and son-in-law?

6 In which Robert Louis Stevenson novel would you encounter Frank Innes?

7 *Or the Astrologer* is the subtitle of which Scott novel?

8 By which nickname was the 19th-century editor Rev Norman Macleod known?

9 Who wrote *A Child's Garden of Verse?*

10 In which Scott novel would you encounter Bailie Nicol Jarvie of Glasgow?

11 Naomi Mitchison's 1947 novel *The Bull Calves* concerns which historical event?

12 In which year was Robert Louis Stevenson born?

13 Edwin Muir was a native of where?

14 Who wrote the novel *The Shipbuilders?*

15 In which Scott novel would you meet Sir Edward Manley?

ANSWERS

GENERAL KNOWLEDGE

1 What happened at Fair Isle South on March 31, 1998, ending a 210-year tradition?

2 Tartan Day, celebrated each April 6 in the United States and Canada, commemorates which historical event?

3 In which year was the QE2 launched?

4 Which aviator is commemorated at a chapel in Ballantrae?

5 Birkhall, near Ballater, was bought by which future king?

6 What is the name of the William Adam house given to the town of Banff by the Duke of Fife?

7 What is the name usually given to the area between Loch Etive and Loch Creran?

8 A monument to which historical figure - and Scott character - stands in Balmaclellan churchyard?

9 Lochs Eck and Long provide shoreline for which large estate?

10 Invernaver National Nature Reserve lies near which Highland village?

11 The ruins of Boghall Castle can be found in which town?

12 How many mainland selochs are there in Scotland (within 3)?

13 What percentage *within 5 per cent* of the Scottish mainland lies more than 500 feet above sea level?

14 For how long has there been tree cover at Glen Affric?

15 How did the Earl of Gowrie die in 1600?

ANSWERS

1. The lighthouse became automated 2. The signing of the Arbroath Declaration 3. 1967 4. Hon Elsie Mackay 5. Edward VII 6. Duff House 7. Benderloch 8. Robert Paterson 9. Benmore 10. Bettyhill 11. Biggar 12. 40 13. 65 14. 10,000 years 15. In the failed plot to kill James VI

PLACES

1   Which 12th-century cathedral was built by Earl Rognvald?

2   Where is Tiumpan Head lighthouse?

3   The Strait of Corryvrecvkam separates which two islands?

4   Where is the bus and rail company Stagecoach based?

5   Where is the Royal Yacht *Britannia* now moored?

6   Which famous historical document was produced at Inchcolm Abbey?

7   Where is Inchcolm Abbey?

8   Which motorway witnessed a 9-mile tailback in 1998 because of a clerical error?

9   On which island is Castle Masil?

10 How many worshippers can Edinburgh's Central Mosque hold?

11 The Hirsel, on the outskirts of Coldstream, is the ancestral home of which family?

12 Where would you find Lochranza?

13 Where would you find the Brus Stone?

14 What does 'Troon' mean?

15 The Sound of Monach lies just west of which Hebridean island?

ANSWERS

1. St Magnus, Kirkwall 2. Lewis 3. Jura and Scarba 4. Perth 5. Leith 6. the *Scotichronicon* 7. On an island in the Firth of Forth 8. The M80 9. Skye 10. 1,200 11. Douglas-Home 12. Arran 13. Annan Town Hall 14. 'Nose', referring to a hook-shaped peninsula 15. North Uist

HISTORY

1 Which king was allowed to retire to France in 1306?

2 In which year did Glasgow hold its highly successful Garden Festival?

3 Saint Bathan was a follower of which other saint?

4 Which Scottish king married Margaret Tudor?

5 In which Dumfries and Galloway town did Reverend Henry Duncan found the first savings bank in 1810?

6 Which Scot was Napoleon's doctor on St Helena?

7 Who was the 'uncrowned king of Scotland' who managed Scotland for Prime Minister William Pitt?

8 Which 15th-century king had eight children by Mary of Guelders?

9 Where did the Fair Maid Lilliard have her legs cut off in battle?

10 Ayr received its first charter from which king?

11 How did Allan Stewart, commandator of Crossraguel Abbey, die in 1570?

12 Mary Fleming of Biggar was a member of which famous 16th-century quartet?

13 Where is the missionary and explorer David Livingstone buried?

14 Dalhousie Castle was besieged unsuccessfully by which English king?

15 In what year was David II crowned?

ANSWERS

1. John Balliol 2. 1988 3. Columba 4. James IV 5. Annan 6. Archibald Arnott 7. Henry Dundas, 1st Viscount Melville 8. James II 9. Lilliard's Edge, Ancrim Moor 10. William the Lion 11. He was roasted by the 4th Earl of Cassilis, who wanted the Abbey lands 12. The Four Marys' (Ladies-in-waiting to Mary, Queen of Scots) 13. Westminster Abbey 14. Henry IV 15. 1331

TRIVIA

1   The missionary Findbarr of Cork gave his name to which island?

2   How did a clerical error in May 1998 create a 9-mile tailback on the M80?

3   Why were some Scottish World Cup fans in France '98 told to wash their faces by French immigration officials?

4   What distinction did the Whaler's Rest, Stornoway, achieve in June 1998?

5   Which distillery was founded in 1798 by a lay preacher who had an illegal still?

6   What was discovered in Cranits, near Kirkwall, in July 1998?

7   What does it mean to wear a kilt 'true'?

8   Who are known as 'Souters'?

9   Which town has more licensed premises per head of population than any other in Scotland?

10 In which year did the Gleneagles Hotel open?

11 Which town is named after Saint Blane of Bute?

12 Whose death sentence was set aside in November 1998?

13 By what means of transport did the Grant family of Orkney travel 12,000 around the world in a seven-year journey that ended in 1998?

14 Who married Anastasia Shirley in Skibo Castle in January 1998?

15 How many Scottish place names contain only two letters?

ANSWERS

1. Barra 2. Motorway resurfacing began at 7am not 7pm 3. To be recognised without saltires on their faces and red wigs 4. It got the island's first Sunday alcohol licence 5. Highland Park 6. A 5000-year-old burial chamber 7. Not to wear underwear 8. Natives of Selkirk 9. Newton Stewart 10. 1924 11. Dunblane 12. Woofie, a collie bitch convicted under the Dangerous Dogs Act 13. Horse-drawn caravan 14. Robert Carlyle 15. Three

TV & ENTERTAINMENT

1 What was the name of Billy Connolly's US TV show, which lasted one season in 1992?

2 Who played McBlane in 'The Fall and Rise of Reginald Perrin'?

3 Who played David Lloyd George in the TV mini-series 'The Treaty'?

4 Maev Alexander was a newsdesk presenter on which television series?

5 Who starred in the title role in the 1947 film *Bonnie Prince Charlie*?

6 Which Hollywood legend starred in the film *Local Hero*?

7 Why does Billy Connolly insist on using the full name Hamilton Academical Football Club when referring to the team?

8 Who starred as the Edinburgh doctor Henry Daniell in the 1945 film *The Body Snatcher*?

9 What was the venue of Frank Sinatra's last Glasgow appearance in 1990?

10 What was the venue of Frank Sinatra's first Glasgow appearance in 1953?

11 The north-east village of Pennan was the location for the shooting of which film?

12 What is the name of Scottish TV's 12.25 slot in Gaelic?

13 At what time does Grampian TV broadcast the news in Gaelic?

14 At what time is *Hope and Gloria* broadcast?

15 At what time does BBC Scotland broadcast *Reporting Scotland*?

ANSWERS

1. 'Billy.' 2. Joseph Brady 3. Ian Bannen 4. 'That's Life!' 5. David Niven 6. Burt Lancaster 7. Because people might think the name is 'Hamilton Academical nil' 8. Boris Karloff 9. Ibrox 10. The Empire Theatre 11. *Local Hero* 12. Telefios 13. 12.25pm 14. 5.30 pm 15. 6.30pm

SPORT

1 In which year did Alex Ferguson leave Aberdeen for Manchester United?

2 Which famous Australian sprint did George McNeill win in 1981?

3 Who was Scotland's first Lonsdale Belt winner?

4 Who became Aberdeen's manager in 1992 following Alex Smith?

5 In which year was the first fight for the British and Empire Welterweight title held in Scotland?

6 Which country did Scotland draw 1-1 with at Hampden Park to qualify for the 1990 World Cup finals?

7 What was the record attendance for a Scottish boxing match?

8 How many international caps did Kenny Dalglish win?

9 In which year did Tom McKean take gold in the 800 metres at the European Championships?

10 In which two events did Dougie Walker take gold in the 1998 European Championships?

11 Who is the only athlete to have defended the *Eric Liddell Memorial* New Year Sprint successfully?

12 Which Prime Minister of Britain won the Derby three times and the 2,000 Guineas twice as a trainer?

13 How many times did trainer Matt Dawson win the Derby?

14 Kenny Dalglish equalled Denis Law's record of goals for his country - how many?

15 Is Perth a flat or jump race course?

ANSWERS

1. 1986 2. Stawell Gift 3. James 'Tancy' Lee in 1915 4. Willie Miller 5. 1928 6. Norway 7. 32,000 (Tommy Milligan v Frank Moody, Carntyne Stadium) 8. 102 9. 1990 10. 4x100 relay and 200 metres 11. Willie McFarlane (1934) 12. The 5th Lord Rosebery 13. Six 14. 30 15. Jump

PEOPLE

1 Where would you find the Thomas Muir Museum?

2 Which later to be ennobled politician served five months' imprisonment in 1919 at Calton Jail as chairman of the Clyde Workers Committee?

3 Which famous writer lived in Entepfuhl?

4 Who wrote the 16th-century work *Ane Satyre of the Thrie Estaits*?

5 Who is known as the 'Father of the Ordnance Survey in Britain'?

6 Which countess held Dunbar Castle for five months against an English siege in 1338?

7 Where did King David II spend the years 1334–41?

8 What post did Ninian Winzet (1518–92) hold?

9 Who founded the Ragged Schools?

10 Where would you find the David Livingstone Centre?

11 Catherine of Braganza was married to which king?

12 Who was the first Anglican bishop of an overseas diocese?

13 Who wrote the 1725 pastoral comedy *The Gentle Shepherd*?

14 Where would you find a museum devoted to E A Hornel?

15 What post did Andrew Melville (1545–1622) hold?

ANSWERS

1 Which poet's collections include *The Expectant Silence?*

2 What is the setting of Naomi Mitchison's historical novel *The Bull Calves?*

3 Who wrote *The Circumjack Cencrastus?*

4 Who wrote the 1932 novel *The Albanach,* concerning the Highland Clearances?

5 Who wrote the novel *The Last of the Lairds?*

6 Who wrote the 1929 novel *White Maa's Saga?*

7 Who created Meg Merilees?

8 Which 16th-century playwright wrote the *Monarchick Tragedies?*

9 Which ten-year period saw the greatest flowering of Sir Walter Scott's work?

10 Whose poetry collections include *The Sinai Sort?*

11 In which Scott novel would you encounter the servant Andrew Fairservice?

12 What were the 'Clark-plays'?

13 What was the pen-name of R G Suthelrand?

14 In which Scott novel would you meet Lady Margaret Bellenden?

15 Who wrote the 1755 play *Douglas?*

ANSWERS

1. William Soutar 2. Gleneagles 3. Hugh MacDiarmid 4. Tom MacDonald 5. John Galt 6. Eric Linklater 7. Sir Walter Scott 8. Sir William Alexander 9. 1814 to 1824 10. Norman McCaig 11. *Rob Roy* 12. popular dramas, often with scriptural subjects 13. Robert Garioch 14. *Old Mortality* 15. John Home

125

GENERAL KNOWLEDGE

1 Dr John Brown, the noted 19th-century author, was born in which town?

2 On which peak are the Allt Coire Eaghainn waterfalls?

3 Between which two geographic features is the bleak moorland known as the Black Mount?

4 Blackness Castle was used as a prison for which group of people in the 17th-century?

5 General Tam Dalyell reorganised the army of which European ruler in the 17th-century?

6 Cummings Tower is the oldest part of which Tayside castle?

7 The Duke of Atholl is head of which clan?

8 Murthly Castle lies 4 miles south-east of which Tayside village?

9 What industrial operation did Sir John Hay introduce to the shores of Loch Maree in 1607?

10 The Castle of Torwoodlee lies south of which Borders village?

11 How many soldiers could be accommodated at the two Roman camps of Ardoch, near Braco, Tayside?

12 Braemar lies in which region?

13 What is Scotland's easternmost point?

14 How did 99 people die at Meikle in 1809?

15 Beinn Sguliaird lies above which Strathclyde town?

ANSWERS

1. Biggar 2. Ben Nevis 3. Loch Tulla and Rannoch Moor 4. Covenanters 5. the Russian tsar 6. Blair 7. Murray 8. Birnam 9. an iron furnace-works 10. Bowland 11. 40,000 12. Grampian 13. Buchan Ness 14. a ferry sank 15. Benderloch

PLACES

1 Of what ecclesiastical curiosity can the island of Great Cumbrae boast?

2 The Skiart Islands lie east of which large Hebridean island?

3 Where did Bonnie Prince Charlie keep prisoners taken at the Battle of Falkirk?

4 What was discovered in 1951 in Arbroath Abbey?

5 Ardchatten, Strathclyde, is associated with whose murder in 1752?

6 Which Lothian town takes its name from a 10th-century Saxon king who was defeated by a combined force of Picts and Scots at a battle there?

7 Auchindown Castle was built partly by which favourite of James III?

8 Which Tayside village is known as 'Musselcrag' in Scott's *The Antiquary*?

9 Which hill, north-east of Balbeggie, is thought to be the site of Macbeth's castle?

10 The twin peaks of Ben Vair lie behind which Highland village?

11 Why was a brewery built at the Highland village of Corpach in 1807?

12 On which island is the Talisker Distillery?

13 Which castle lies opposite the island of Eriska?

14 Where is Lochan Meall-an-t-Suidhe?

15 Near which Highland village is Neptune's Staircase?

ANSWERS

1. Britain's smallest cathedral 2. Lewis 3. Doune Castle 4. The Stone of Destiny 5. The 'Red Fox' 6. Athelstaneford 7. Thomas Cochrane 8. Auchmithie 9. Dunsinane Hill 10. Ballachulish 11. To woo labourers on the Caledonian Canal away from whisky 12. Skye 13. Barcaldine 14. On the slopes of Ben Nevis 15. Banavie

HISTORY

1   Which 15th-century king had eight children by Joan Beaufort ?

2   Who created the slogan 'Glasgow's Miles Better'?

3   What nickname did the 18th-century Lord Braxfield earn?

4   In which year was the Scots Dyke constructed to provide a recognised boundary between Scotland and England?

5   Which two ethnic groups immigrated to the mining area of Carfin in the 19th century?

6   How many times did Mary, Queen of Scots marry?

7   Which 18th-century soldier devised the first Ordnance Survey maps?

8   What was significant about the Raid of Keidswire in 1575?

9   Near which Borders village was the Roman camp known as Ad Fines?

10 Which Scottish king married Margaret, daughter of Henry III of England?

11 What was the former name of Castle Douglas?

12 In which year was the first ship launched from Clydebank shipyards?

13 Which pair of Govan brothers set up the first Clydebank shipyards?

14 Which canal was built in the late 18th-century to carry coal to Glasgow?

15 Which unpopular ruler was known as 'Toom Tabard' (empty coat) by the Scots?

ANSWERS

1. James I 2. Michael Kelly 3. The Hanging Judge 4. 1552 5. Irish and Poles 6. Three 7. Major-General William Roy 8. It was the last positive Border conflict between Scotland and England 9. Carter Bar 10. Alexander III 11. Causewayend 12. 1872 13. James and George Thomson 14. Monkland Canal 15. John Balliol

1 How many species of deer are there in Scotland?

2 Which is the shortest scheduled flight in the world?

3 Within one minute, how long does this flight last?

4 How much distance does this scheduled flight cover, within one mile/kilometre?

5 What British record does the Star Hotel, Moffat, hold?

6 How long is a traditional Scottish mile?

7 Which Scottish king practised dentistry?

8 Complete the following: Oa, Ae...?

9 How did Edinburgh's Witches Well get its name?

10 Which 19th-century Glasgow tea trader controlled one-tenth of the entire tea trade?

11 In which century did golf arrive in Scotland from Holland?

12 In which two Scottish regions can you find a river Dee?

13 Which disease devastated Edinburgh in 1645?

14 What does the 'celidh' translate as?

15 Does heather thrive on acid or alkaline soil?

ANSWERS

1. Five 2. From Westray to Papa Westray, Orkneys 3. One minute, 14 Seconds 4. One and a half miles/2.4 km 5. Britain's narrowest hotel (20 feet/6 m) 6. 1,984 yards/1814 m 7. James IV 8. Bu: Scotland's other place name containing only three letters 9. More than 300 witches were burnt there between 1479 and 1722 10. Thomas Lipton 11. 15th 12. Grampian and Galloway 13. Bubonic plague 14. Visit 15. Acid

TV & ENTERTAINMENT

1 Which popular actor worked as a research scientist before becoming an actor?

2 Who played Lady Virginia Bellamy in 'Upstairs, Downstairs'?

3 With which American comedienne did Billy Connolly tour the United States in 1990?

4 Which event in 1988 inspired Ricky Ross of Deacon Blue to write 'Don't Let the Teardrops Start'?

5 Who took 'Ally's Tartan Army' to number 6 in the charts in 1978?

6 What song, from 1981, was the highest chart success for Altered Images?

7 Scotland's first film featured which leader?

8 What was the Eurhythmics' first chart hit?

9 Who asked 'Donald where's your troosers' in 1960?

10 Which Scottish actor won a 1998 Tony Award for his role in the Broadway production of *Cabaret*?

11 Who is the Scot who founded Creation Records?

12 Which Glasgow studio is the largest independent television and film studio in Scotland?

13 Who had successful West End and Broadway runs starring in *Whose Life Is It Anyway*??

14 Which television actress is the seventh of twelve children born to parents who eloped to Buenos Airies before returning to settle in Greenock?

15 Which Irvine-born TV weather forecaster has written *Great British Obsession?*

ANSWERS

1. Richard Wilson 2. Hannah Gordon 3. Whoopie Goldberg 4. Jim Sillars' SNP by-election victory in Glasgow Govan 5. Andy Cameron 6. 'Happy Birthday' 7. Queen Victoria at Balmoral (1895) 8. 'Sweet dreams are made of this' (1983) 9. Andy Stewart 10. Alan Cumming 11. Alan McGee 12. Blackcat 13. Tom Conti 14. Stella Gonet 15. Francis Wilson

1 Which Scottish woman had the fastest marathon debut (2 hours, 27.32 minutes) in the New York Marathon?

2 Who was the first Scot to referee a World Heavyweight Title fight?

3 Which two boxers fought for the title in that fight?

4 Who was the captain of the Wembley Wizards?

5 Who scored the hat-trick in that 5-1 defeat of England?

6 What was Alex James's famous comment after the match?

7 Who was Celtic's goalkeeper in the 1967 European Cup final?

8 Which team won the Scottish Cup in each of its first three seasons?

9 Why wasn't the Scottish Cup won by anyone in 1990?

10 At which weight did Jackie Paterson win the world title in 1943?

11 Which Scottish boxer has held the most titles in a career?

12 In which year did the first Soviet jockey win a race in Britain?

13 Where was the first professional boxing match filmed for cinema viewing?

14 In which year did the match take place?

15 Who was the first woman in the UK to become Clerk of the Course?

ANSWERS

1. Liz McColgan 2. George Smith, in 1966 3. Henry Cooper and Muhammad Ali 4. Jimmy McMullan 5. Alan Morton 6. 'We could have had ten' 7. Ronnie Simpson 8. Queen's Park 9. It was withheld following a riot between Rangers and Celtic fans 10. Flyweight 11. Alex 'Bud' Watson (ten titles) 12. 1990 (Mogamed Tokov at Maxwell Motors Glasnost Hurdle), Kelso 13. Industrial Hall, Annandale Street, Edinburgh 14. 1924 15. Morag Chalmers (Ayr)

PEORLE

16

PEOPLE

1 Where would you find Barrie's Birthplace?

2 Which cardinal was assassinated at Saint Andrews in 1546?

3 Which Jesuit priest, executed in 1615 for denying Royal Supremacy, was beatified by the Catholic Church?

4 Which king, a cousin of the Earl of Northumbria, was killed by Macbeth near Elgin in 1040?

5 What was Queen Margaret's (reigned 1286-90) nickname?

6 How old was she when she died?

7 Where is she buried?

8 Who founded the Iona Community?

9 The brother of which Archbishop of Canterbury was Moderator of the General Assembly of the Church of Scotland?

10 Where would you find the Wiliam Lamb Memorial Studio?

11 Who is the only man to have held an officer's rank in the British, American and Russian navies?

12 What virtual event did Dr Bill Lumsden of Glenmorangie, West Lothian, organise in 1997?

13 Which award did Fr William Anderson of St Mary's Cathedral, Aberdeen, earn in in 1996?

14 For which philanthropic activity is Willaim Quarrier best remembered?

15 Which 16th-century Principal of St Leonard's College, St Andrews, was reckoned to be the best Latin poet in Europe?

ANSWERS

1. Kirriemuir 2. David Beaton 3. John Ogilvie 4. Duncan 5. The Maid of Norway 6. Eight 7. Bergen 8. Lord Macleod of Fuinary 9. Cosmo Gordon Lang 10. Montrose 11. John Paul Jones 12. A whisky tasting on the Internet 13. Preacher of the Year 14. Founding Quarrier's Orphans Homes 15. George Buchanan

MUSIC & LITERATURE

1 Who created the character Elspeth Mucklebait?

2 Who founded the Macmillan Press?

3 How are the novels *Sunset Song, Cloud Howe* and *Grey Granite,* by Lewis Grassic Gibbon, known collectively?

4 In which Scott novel would you meet Sir Frederick Langley?

5 In which Scott novel does Mrs Saddletree appear?

6 Who wrote the poem 'The Little General', set in Orkney?

7 What is crambo-jingle?

8 The half-witted Peter Peebles appears in which Scott novel?

9 The Glasgow Repertory Theatre was influenced by which Dublin theatre in the early 20th century?

10 Which Scottish playwright has written the play *Knives in Hens?*

11 Who is the director of the Traverse Theatre?

12 Which David Greir play calls for an on-stage string quartet?

13 With which repertory group is David Maclennan associated?

14 In which Scott novel would you encounter Lady Augusta de Berkely?

15 What is a 'big ha' Bible'?

ANSWERS

1. Sir Walter Scott 2. David Macmillan 3. The Scots Quair Trilogy 4. *The Black Dwarf)* 5. *The Heart of Midlothian* 6. Edwin Muir 7. Ad lib rhyming 8. *Redgauntlet* 9. The Abbey Theatre 10. David Harrower 11. Philip Howard 12. *Timeless* 13. Wild Cat Theatre Group 14. *Castle Dangerous* 15. A hereditary copy of the Bible in a household

GENERAL KNOWLEDGE

1   On which island could you find the oldest rocks in the world?

2   What type of rocks are they?

3   How old are they?

4   The year 1499 saw the first recorded documentation of what in the Exchequer Rolls of Scotland?

5   What is the northernmost point on the Pennine Way?

6   What is the greatest north-south distance in Scotland?

7   What title was held by Thomas Barry, who in 1570 had his right hand cut off for forging the Regent's signature?

8   Which town is the centre of the Ochil Hills woollen industry?

9   Which American naval hero was born at Arbigland, where his father was gardener?

10   In which year did the Macdonalds forfeit the Lordship of the Isles to the Scottish Crown?

11   Within 25, how many islands are there in the Western Isles?

12   What is the greatest east-west distance in Scotland?

13   Which town is nearest to Kailzie Gardens?

14   What is Glomach?

15   An English Act of 1548 ensured that how many days would be allowed for the steeping and drying of barley when making malt whisky?

ANSWERS

1. Lewis 2. Archaen Gneiss 3. Almost 3,000 million years old 4. 'Aqua vitae' 5. Kirk Yetholm 6. 275 miles/443 km 7. Unicorn Pursuivant 8. Tillicoultry 9. John Paul Jones 10. 1493 11. 550 12. 154 miles/248 km 13. Peebles 14. A waterfall with a 400-foot/122 m leap 15. 17

1. Which poet composed some of his most famous works at Eliisland Farm, Auldgirth?

2. Ruined Ardsinchar Castle lies in which resort?

3. In which Grampian village is the Brig o' Feugh ?

4. The island of Eriska lies in which loch?

5. What are found in abundance at Strath Never, near Bettyhill, Highlands?

6. Biggar Water is a tributary of which river?

7. White Coomb stands over which Dumfries and Galloway town?

8. Buchan Ness, the furthest point east in Scotland, lies near which Grampian village?

9. The Binns, a 15th century mansion, was once linked by underground passage with which castle?

10. The Millbuie is a ridge running through which peninsula?

11. Blackshiels lies on the edge of which hills?

12. Which tragedy prompted Thomas Telford to build the Bonar Bridge in the Highlands?

13. Which pass was long known as the 'Mouth of the Highlands'?

14. Where would you find Cadger's Brig?

15. On which island is Glen Brittle Forest?

ANSWERS

1. Robert Burns 2. Ballantrae 3. Banff 4. Creran 5. Prehistoric ruins 6. Tweed 7. Birkhill 8. Boddam 9. Blackness 10. Black Isle 11. Lammermuir 12. The Meikle Ferry Disaster of 1809 13. Birnam Pass 14. Biggar 15. Skye

135

1 In which year did Mary, Queen of Scots abdicate?

2 What title did Clan Donald assume in 1354?

3 Which Scottish ruler was born in the Castle of Buittle in 1249?

4 Where did King David II convalesce after being wounded and captured at Neville in 1346?

5 Which king died in Dundonald Castle in 1390?

6 Which king died in Dundonald Castle in 1406?

7 Whose son Alexander was known as 'the Wolf of Badenoch'?

8 What was the Twapenny Faith?

9 The importing of what type of books was prohibited by the Scottish Parliament in 1525?

10 Where did King James V marry?

11 In which year was the 'Beggar's Summons' posted on friars' houses?

12 What was this document?

13 Who wrote *Wallace* between 1470 and 1480?

14 Which king was described by his son as being *rex togatus,* or a 'king in civvies'?

15 Which king financed a mission to find *quinta essencia,* the alchemists' goal for producing gold?

ANSWERS

1. 1567 2. Lord of the Isles 3. John Balliol 4. Bambургh 5. Robert II 6. Robert III 7. Robert II 8. A Catholic catechism of 1559 9. Lutheran 10. Notre-Dame Cathedral, Paris 11. 1559 12. A challenge to the friars to come out and do honest work 13. Blind Harry 14. James III 15. James IV

136

1 Paisley was once the world's largest producer of which household item?

2 Which founder of the American conservation movement was born in Dunbarton in 1838?

3 Which country has received the most Scottish immigrants?

4 Which country ranks second in this regard?

5 Which Scottish emblem was adopted after a combined Scot/Pict victory over the Saxons in the tenth century?

6 The Queen's View over Loch Lomond commemorates Queen Victoria's first sight of the loch in which year?

7 What is Neptune's Staircase?

8 Near which Strathclyde resort is the Nick o' Balloch Pass?

9 What is the highest point on the Carlisle to Glasgow road?

10 Which reservoir lies just north-east of Beith?

11 Complete this rhyme: 'Tide, tide what'er betide. Haig shall be Haig of...'

12 What feat was accomplished on Ben Nevis in 1911 and 1961?

13 Which Highland village was founded by Elizabeth, Marchioness of Stafford, for crofters evicted during the Highland Clearances?

14 Where is the Celtic bell known as the Ronnel Bell?

15 Ardneanach is another name for which Black Isle ridge?

ANSWERS

1. Thread 2. John Muir 3. Canada 4. Australia 5. St Andrew's Cross 6. 1869 7. A series of eight locks on the Caledonian Canal 8. Barr 9. Beattock Summit 10. Threepwood 11. Bemersyde 12. A car drove to the summit 13. Bettyhill 14. Birnie 15. Millbuie

TV & ENTERTAINMENT

1 Who played Billy MacGregor in the US TV series 'Head of the Class'?

2 How many members of Lloyd Cole and the Commotions are not Scottish?

3 Which Scottish group recorded 'Ebeneezer Goode'?

4 Which song, from 1983, was the last chart hit for Altered Images?

5 'A Scottish Soldier', from 1961, was whose best-selling record?

6 Which company made the first advertising film?

7 Which song did Nazareth take to number 9 in 1973?

8 Which group took 'Keep on dancing' to number 9 in the charts in 1971?

9 Where did the first British concert featuring ten pianos take place?

10 In which year did the Average White Band have a number 6 hit with 'Pick Up the Pieces'?

11 In which year did the TV series 'Bad Boys' debut?

12 What was Big Country's first chart hit, in 1983?

13 'Doctor Finlay' made an appearance in a mini-series of what year?

14 In which year did the TV version of *Highlander* first appear as a series?

15 Which record label was founded by Glasgow Slam DJs Stuart and Orde?

ANSWERS

15. Soma

9. Bute Hall, Glasgow (1990) 10. 1975 11. 1996 12. 'Fields of Fire' 13. 1993 14. 1992
5. Andy Stewart 6. Haig's Scotch Whisky (1897) 7. 'Broken Down Angel' 8. Bay City Rollers
1. Billy Connolly 2. One - Lloyd Cole 3. The Shamen 4. 'Don't talk to me about love'

SPORT

1 Which runner holds the Scottish women's records at 1500 metres, the mile, 2000 metres, 3000 metres and 5000 metres?

2 At which weight did Ken Buchanan win the world title in 1970?

3 Who scored Celtic's winner in the 1967 European Cup final?

4 Who scored Scotland's first goal?

5 At which weight did Jim Higgins win a Lonsdale Belt in record time?

6 Who was Scotland's manager for the 1967 3-2 defeat of England?

7 In which years did Tommy Armour win the US PGA title?

8 Which team did Celtic beat 6-1 in the 1972 Scottish Cup Final?

9 Gordon Cosh has represented Britain in which sport?

10 At which weight was Benny Lynch British, European and World Champion?

11 Which was Jock Stein's first club as a manager?

12 Which was Jock Stein's second club as a manager?

13 Which top-flight runner has been awarded a prize for best regional dialect *Dundonian*?

14 In which two years did Alex 'Bud' Watson win the ABA light-heavyweight title?

15 In which year did the Scottish horse Merryman win the Grand National?

ANSWERS

1. Yvonne Murray 2. Lightweight 3. Steve Chalmers 4. Denis Law 5. Bantamweight 6. Bobby Brown 7. 1924 and 1930 8. Hibernian 9. Golf (Walker Cup) 10. Flyweight 11. Dunfermline 12. Hibernian 13. Liz McColgan 14. 1945 and 1947 15. 1960

PEOPLE

1   What was the 13th-century wizard Michael Scott accused of having brought to Scotland?

2   Whose ship was the *Bonhomme Richard?*

3   Who wrote *Autumnal Rambles Along the Scottish Mountains?*

4   Dr James Craik of Kirkbeam founded whose medical service?

5   Helen Walker of Kirkpatrick was the prototype of which Scott heroine?

6   Who founded the Reformed Presbyterian Church?

7   John Paton, of Torthorwald, was a missionary to which islands?

8   Brian Hope Taylor excavated which medieval earthwork in the 1930s?

9   The 'four knights of Eskdale' were brothers from which Dumfries and Galloway village?

10 Who became Lord Home of The Hirsel?

11 Sir John Pirie of Duns held which high position in England in the mid-1800s?

12 What was Sir Thomas Leaman's more famous nickname?

13 Which saint rids Innerleithen of snakes each year?

14 'Bowed David Ritchie', who lived near Kirkton, was the model for which Scott title character?

15 Which advocate, who died in 1817, was known as 'the best-loved man in Scotland'?

ANSWERS

1. The Plague 2. John Paul Jones 3. Rev Thomas Grierson 4. The US Army 5. Jeannie Deans 6. Rev James Macmillan 7. New Hebrides 8. The Motte of Urr 9. White Hill 10. Sir Alec Douglas Home 11. Lord-Mayor of London 12. Thomas the Rhymer 13. Ronan 14. *The Black Dwarf* 15. Henry Erskine

MUSIC & LITERATURE

1 Which young playwright has written *Passing Places*?

2 A poem celebrating 'yill' concerns what?

3 Who wrote the 1933 historical novel *Campbell of Duisk*?

4 Which Robert Louis Stevenson novel was published in the same year as *Doctor Jekyll and Mr Hyde*?

5 Who wrote the 1923 play *The Glen is Mine*?

6 What does 'unco' mean in Lallands?

7 What does 'wimplin' mean in Burns's poetry?

8 Who wrote the 14th-century work *The Bruce*?

9 Whose poem *Shipwrecked* is the first long sea-poem in English?

10 What was the name of the group of writers who rallied around David Hume?

11 What does 'linkin' mean in Burns's poetry?

12 Who wrote the 1901 novel *The House with Green Shutters*?

13 *Gillespie* is whose only novel?

14 Who is credited with coining Edinburgh's nickname 'Ould Reekie'?

15 In which Scott novel would you encounter Darsie Latimer?

ANSWERS

1. Stephen Greenhorn 2. Ale 3. Robert Craig 4. *Kidnapped* 5. John Brandane 6. Too, or very 7. Meandering 8. John Barbour 9. William Falconer 10. The Literati 11. Hurrying 12. George Douglas Brown 13. J MacDougall Hay 14. Robert Ferguson 15. *Redgauntlet*

1   The Guild of Surgeon Barbers, on its creation, was given the monopoly for the manufacture of what?

2   Which body of water did 19th-century guidebooks refer to as 'The German Channel'?

3   What is the oldest inhabited house in Scotland?

4   Which poet was born in Mellerstain House?

5   Who, in military parlance, was a 'souter'?

6   How long, within 20 miles, is the Southern Upland Way?

7   How old was Robert Burns when he died?

8   What type of geographical feature is Reekie Linn?

9   Where are the oldest standing gasworks in Britain?

10 What, in military parlance, was the 'bassin'?

11 What, in Edinburgh, is 'haar'?

12 Granite from Ailsa Craig was traditionally used to make what type of sporting equipment?

13 Rozelle House is in which Strathclyde town?

14 A mort safe would be used to guard against what?

15 Who, in an 18th-century cavalry troop, was the 'cornet'?

ANSWERS

1. Aqua vitae 2. The North Sea 3. Traquair, Tweeddale 4. Thomas the Rhymer 5. The standard bearer 6. 212 miles/341 km 7. 37 8. A waterfall 9. Biggar 10. The colours 11. A damp mist 12. Curling stones 13. Alloway 14. Grave-robbery 15. The youngest leader

PLACES

1   The River Awe enters Loch Etive near which Strathclyde town?

2   The Dumfries and Galloway village of Borgine was the setting for which Sir Walter Scott novel?

3   The 4,241-foot Cairn Toul stands above which Grampian resort?

4   The Bridge of Balgie lies along which glen?

5   The Quarrier's Orphan Homes are located just outside which Strathclyde residential district?

6   Doune Castle, near Sterling, was built by which 14th-century duke?

7   For what is Pitmedden chiefly noted?

8   Which industry is commemorated at the Eyemouth Museum?

9   Which king is credited with having founded Cambuskenneth Abbey?

10 Brodick Castle on the Isle of Arran was for generations the estate of which Dukes?

11 Glasgow's Burrell Art collection lies in the grounds of which house?

12 William Murdoch, the 18th-century pioneer of gas lighting, was born in which town?

13 Bonhill House, Bonhill, belonged to which 18th-century novelist and satirist?

14 Garbh-Allt Falls are near which famous resort?

15 Which town is nearest to the castles of Kirkhall and Knockdolian?

ANSWERS

1. Bonawe 2. *The Master of Ballantrae* 3. Braemar 4. Glen Lyon 5. Bridge of Weir 6. Robert Stewart, Duke of Albany 7. Its famous garden 8. The fishing industry 9. David I 10. Dukes of Hamilton 11. Pollok House 12. Auchinleck 13. Tobias Smollett 14. Braemar 15. Ballantrae

1 Which ruler of Scotland was married to Isabella de Warenne, daughter of the Earl of Surrey?

2 What was the 16th-century publication *Patrick's Places?*

3 What name did Queen Victoria use in order to travel around Scotland incognito?

4 Which unmarried king was nicknamed 'the Maiden'?

5 Which king was kidanpped at sea by the English when he was 11 years old?

6 Who had Lady Glamis burnt for on a charge of witchcraft in 1537?

7 Which 16th-century scholar went to Malmo, Sweden, to translate Lutheran works into Scots?

8 Which city was often descibed as 'the second Alexandria'?

9 James V's failure to meet whom in York in September 1541 led to an invasion of Scotland?

10 What, in medieval terms, was the 'cocket' of a Royal Burgh?

11 Which English king burnt the abbeys of Melrose and Dryburgh in 1385?

12 Why did he do this?

13 Which king gave up the northern counties of England to Henry II?

14 Which king died of fever on the island of Kerrera and was buried in Melrose?

15 Which king died in theBattle of Lumphanan in 1057?

ANSWERS

1. John Balliol 2. a Protestant catechism 3. The Countess of Balmoral 4. Malcolm IV 5. James V 6. James I 7. John Gau 8. Berwick 9. Henry VIII 10. its seal 11. Richard II 12. in reprisal for French troops entering Scotland 13. Malcolm IV 14. Alexander II 15. Macbeth

1 Which castle is often called Ship Castle because of its shape?

2 How many Scottish castles were left fortified after the Articles of Union?

3 Why is the parish church of Kilmarrow, Islay, round?

4 Braemar Castle overlooks which river?

5 The Lee Penny Amulet is associated with which Scott novel?

6 In which Grampian village do residents burn the Clave each year?

7 What takes place during the Burning of the Clave?

8 Which composer stayed at Cochran Castle in 1848, shortly before his death?

9 On which island is the Oa Peninsula?

10 How many Paps of Jura are there?

11 In which town near Paisley can you see a statue to the 16th-century piper Habbie Simpson?

12 Three members of which Ayrshire family have been governor-generals of New Zealand?

13 Where is Scotland's Mother Masonic Lodge?

14 Why did James IV invite the Dutch and Germans to Leadhill in the 16th-century?

15 Old Yule falls on which date each year?

ANSWERS

1. Blackness Castle 2. Four 3. So the Devil won't be able to hide in a corner 4. Dee 5. *The Talisman* 6. Burghead 7. A tar-filled barrel is set alight and rolled downhill to ward off evil spirits 8. Chopin 9. Islay 10. Three 11. Kilbarchan 12. Ferguson 13. Kilwinning 14. To prospect for gold 15. 11 January

TV & ENTERTAINMENT

1 Which was the only number one hit for Annie Lennox?

2 Which of Sir Walter Scott's novels was turned into a popular TV mini-series in 1997?

3 Who took 'Bang bang' to number two in the charts in 1979?

4 What was Bronski Beat's first chart hit, in 1984?

5 Which Midge Ure song holds the record for the shortest time between the recording and the record entering the shops?

6 Within five, how many hours did this process take?

7 Which two Bay City Rollers songs went to number one in 1975?

8 In which year did the TV series 'Taggart' first screen?

9 With which other singer did Barbara Dickson duet on the number one hit 'I know him so well' in 1985?

10 Which of Donovan's records went highest in the charts?

11 In which year did the BBC do a TV version of *As You Like It,* filmed in Scotland?

12 In which year did Andy Stewart's 'Dr Finlay' enter the charts twice?

13 What record did Dave Sheriff achieve in Inverness between February 17 and 25, 1989?

14 How was the film *The Big Man* known on its US release?

15 Who sang the number 9 hit 'Answer Me' in 1976?

ANSWERS

1. 'There Must Be An Angel' (1985) 2. *Ivanhoe* 3. B A Robertson 4. 'Smalltown boy' 5. 'Dear God' 6. 81 7. 'Bye Bye Baby' and 'Give a Little Love' 8. 1983 9. Elaine Paige 10. 'Sunshine Superman' (no 2 in 1966) 11. 1978 12. 1965 13. The longest session by a one-man band 14. *Crossing the Line* 15. Barbara Dickson

SPORT

1   At which weight did Walter McGowan win the world title in 1966?

2   Which English club did Jock Stein briefly manage between Celtic and Scotland?

3   Which Scottish golfer won three of the four Grand Slams?

4   What is the name of the Ayrshire mining village where Bill Shankly was born?

5   In which Lanarkshire mining village was Matt Busby born?

6   In which year did the Scottish horse Licius win the Grand National?

7   Which great Middleweight title fight did Eugene Henderson referee in 1951?

8   Which two Grand Slams has Sandy Lyle won?

9   In what year did Bill Shankly become manager of Liverpool?

10   Where was ten-time Scottish boxing champion Alex 'Bud' Watsoni born?

11   How many international caps did Matt Busby win as a player?

12   Which was the first top-flight boxing match-up between an American and a Scot?

13   In the 1978 World Cup Finals in Argentina, Scotland lost to Peru and beat Holland. Which team did they draw with?

14   Which runner set the European women's 2000-metre record in 1994?

15   What was her time?

ANSWERS

1. Flyweight 2. Leeds Utd 3. Tommy Armour 4. Glenbuck 5. Orbiston 6. 1978 7. Sugar Ray Robinson v Randolph Turpin 8. The Open and the Masters 9. 1959 10. Leith 11. One 12. Augie Ratner v Johnny Brown 13. Iran 14. Yvonne Murray 15. 5 minutes, 26.93 seconds

PEOPLE

1. Who built a dynamite facory at Ardeer in 1843?

2. What title did James Boswell's father Alexander hold?

3. Which clan tried and failed to ambush Robert the Bruce in 1308?

4. Who built the Crinan Canal in 1793-1801?

5. Which 14th-century nobleman as known as the 'Guid Schir James'?

6. How did Jeannie Cameron become famous in the mid-18th century?

7. Which Gaelic scholar created Port Ellen in 1821?

8. With which sport do you associate the Marquis of Ailsa?

9. Saint Serf is said to have brought up which famous saint?

10. Which author's house was the Mount, near Cupar?

11. With which Commonwealth country is the Fergusson family of Ayrshire associated?

12. What profession was Niel Gow the Elder?

13. Who wrote *Palice of Honour* in 1501?

14. With which art was the 13th-century ecclesiastic Simon Tailler associated?

15. David, Earl of Huntingdon, founded which abbey in 1178?

ANSWERS

1. Alfred Nobel 2. Lord Auchinleck 3. MacDougalls 4. John Rennie 5. Sir James Douglas 6. As an influence on Jacobite politics 7. W F Campbell of Islay 8. Golf 9. Mungo (or Kentigern) 10. Sir David Lindsay 11. New Zealand (as governors-general) 12. Composer 13. Gavin Douglas 14. Music 15. Lindores

1　Which poet produced the collection *Hamewith*?

2　In which century did the poet Robert Henryson write?

3　Who wrote *A Drunk Man Looks at The Thistle* in 1926

4　Who wrote the novel *The Deans*?

5　In which Scott novel would you encounter Captain John Porteous?

6　Who wrote the line 'A fig for those by law protected'?

7　Whose autobiography was entitled *The Man on my Back*?

8　William Dunbar was the leading poet during whose reign?

9　Who wrote the play *The Golden Legend of Shults*?

10　Which 13,500-line epic predated Chaucer's work?

11　Who wrote *Dialogues Concerning Natural Religion* in 1779?

12　What was the Easy Club?

13　Which unfinished novel was Robert Louis Stevenson writing when he died?

14　In which Scott novel would you meet Isabella Vere?

15　*Caledonia Dreaming* is the work of which young Scottish playwright?

ANSWERS

1. Charles Murray 2. 15th 3. Hugh MacDiarmid 4. Dot Allan 5. *Heart of Midlothian* 6. Robert Burns 7. Eric Linklater 8. James IV 9. James Bridie 10. *The Bruce* 11. David Hume 12. An 18th-century literary society 13. *Weir of Hermiston* 14. *The Black Dwarf* 15. David Greig

18

1 Who, according to Borders legend, sleep below Scott's view?

2 Which notorious Victorian writer spent his last years at a cottage in Polton, Lothian?

3 A Scottish ale brewed in Broughton takes its name from which John Buchan novel?

4 Standing stones known as the Taxing Stone and Long Tom lie near which Dumfries and Galloway town?

5 Threave Wildfowl Refuge lies along which river?

6 The *Lusitania* was launched from which shipyard?

7 Summerlee (Industrial) Heritage Park can be found in which Strathclyde town?

8 Which Robert Adam-designed castle was built for the 10th Earl of Cassilis in the late 18th-century?

9 What distinction can the Cathedral of the Isles, Millport, claim?

10 Which army was defeated at Airds Mons in 1679?

11 According to Thomas the Rhymer, whose grave lies at the confluence of the Drumelzier Burn and the River Tweed?

12 What job did Robert Burns take on arrival in Dumfries in 1791?

13 A sculpture park featuring works by Epstein, Rodin and Moore stands by which reservoir?

14 How many Scottish islands are inhabited?

15 The Guild of Surgeon Barbers was created in which year: a)1509, b)1566, c)1622?

ANSWERS

1   Which is the deepest cave in Scotland?

2   On which island is the Trotternish Peninsula?

3   What is the most northerly town on the Scottish mainland?

4   Where is Scotland's only Buddhist temple?

5   Which is the shortest street in Scotland?

6   Where was Scotland's first aluminium plant?

7   Where would you find a street nicknamed the Khyber Pass?

8   Which is the 'Honest Town'?

9   Which is the 'Fair City'?

10 Where is Hielanman's Umbrella?

11 Which is the western end of the Southern Upland Way?

12 Which is the eastern end of the Southern Upland Way?

13 Which island is nicknamed the Misty Isle?

14 Which is the deepest inland lake in Britain?

15 Within 100 feet, how deep is it at its deepest?

ANSWERS

1. Cnoc nan Uamh 2. Skye 3. Thurso 4. Eskdalemuir 5. Chapel Street, Moffat 6. Fort William 7. Stromness, Orkney 8. Musselburgh 9. Perth 10. Argyll Street, Glasgow, passing under Central Station 11. Portpatrick 12. Cockburnspath 13. Skye 14. Loch Morar 15. 1,077 feet/328 m

HISTORY

1. Where did William the Lion die?

2. Anne of Denmark married which Scottish king?

3. Under which king were hereditary lordships of Parliament created?

4. Who led the English to victory at Pinkie in 1547?

5. Whose death in 1537 prompted the first public mourning in Scotland?

6. What was the nickname of the 5th Earl of Angus, who burnt Dryburgh in 1480?

7. The Spanish ambassador Pedro de Ayala was assigned to whose court?

8. The Maid of Norway died on her way to marry whom?

9. In what year was the English Regent Albany's 'Foul Riad' on Scotland?

10. To which London palace was the body of James IV taken?

11. Which pretender to the English throne was received by James IV in 1495?

12. Which king received the Papal Cape of Maintenance and Sword of Honour in 1507?

13. In which year was King's College, Aberdeen, founded?

14. Which king's second wife was Marie de Couci?

15. For how many years was there an Interregnum in Scotland at the end of the 13th-century?

ANSWERS

1. Stirling 2. James VI (James I of England) 3. James II 4. Protector Somerset 5. Madeleine, wife of James V 6. Bell-the-cat 7. James IV 8. Prince Edward of England 9. 1416 10. Sheen 11. Perkin Warbeck 12. James IV 13. 1495 14. Alexander II 15. ten

1   The island of Luing has a bridge 'across the Atlantic' to where?

2   What is 'machair'?

3   Why did the weavers of Newmilns receive a Stars and Stripes banner in the mid-19th century?

4   Where was the first Nelson Monument erected?

5   The son of which famous literary figure died in Scotland's last recognised duel?

6   In which Fife village is there a 16th-century carving of 'The Provost' cheerfully holding a toby jug?

7   Which classical sculptures are associated with the country estate Broomhall?

8   How long did the first production of Lindsay's 'Ane Satire on the Thrie Estaits' last in the 16th-century?

9   What was Scotland's first 'New town'?

10   Which whisky held the House of Commons contract in the 1920s?

11   Which sacred work washed up on the shores of Whithorn in the 880s?

12   How were the Wigtown Martyrs executed?

13   'Remember Broomhouse' was a Scottish rallying cry at which battle of 1545?

14   Who was known as 'Mr Evidence'?

15   What sort of person is a 'drouth'?

ANSWERS

1. The Scottish mainland 2. Sandy turf 3. In recognition to their address of support for President Lincoln during the US Civil War 4. Taynuilt 5. James Boswell 6. Ceres 7. The Elgin Marbles (seat of the Earls of Elgin) 8. Nine hours 9. East Kilbride 10. Tyronkirk 11. The Lindisfarne Gospel 12. Being tied to a stake and left to drown in the incoming tide 13. Ancrum Moor 14. John Murray of Broughton 15. One who likes a drink

TV & ENTERTAINMENT

1 Who sang 'The Battle's O'er' in 1961?

2 Which 1996 film centres on an emotionally repressed young woman's search for sexual fulfilment in a deeply religious Highland community?

3 Which 1983 TV series used Aberdeen as a location setting for Moscow?

4 With which song did the Chimes reach number 9 in the charts in 1990?

5 In which year was *Eye of the Needle,* filmed largely in Scotland, released?

6 Sir Herbert Beerbohm Tree and Constance Collier starred in a 1915 film version of which play?

7 Which Scottish singer/comedian had a number one hit with 'D.I.V.O.R.C.E.' in 1975?

8 In which year was the film *Greyfriars Bobby* released?

9 Which group had a top ten hit with 'Bad Bad Boy' in 1973?

10 Which 1981 film used 'dialogue' by Anthony Burgess to re-create the likely speech patterns of prehistoric people?

11 Which *Highlander* film was called 'The Sorcerer'?

12 Which group took 'Somewhere in My Heart' to number 3 in the charts in 1988?

13 Which 1983 film thriller set in Moscow used Scottish locations?

14 Derek Jacobi appeared in which TV mini-series, based on a historical novel, in 1997?

15 In which year did Altered Images take 'I Could Be Happy' to number 7 in the charts?

ANSWERS

1. Andy Stewart 2. *Breaking the Waves* 3. 'An Englishman Abroad' 4. 'I still haven't found what I'm looking for' 5. 1981 6. *Macbeth* 7. Billy Connolly 8. 1961 9. Nazareth 10. *Quest for Fire* 11. *Highlander III* 12. Aztec Camera 13. *Gorky Park* 14. 'Ivanhoe' 15. 1981

154

1 Within 50, how many winners has Willie Carson ridden in Britain?

2 Which runner holds the women's world 3000-metre record?

3 Which defender captained Rangers and Scotland in the 50s and 60s, and broke his leg in his last game for Scotland, against England in 1963?

4 At which weight did Jim Watt win the World Title in 1979?

5 Which was the only team other than Rangers or Celtic to win the Scottish Cup during the 1960s?

6 Michael Bonallack has represented Britain internationally in which sport?

7 What is the name of East Stirling's home ground?

8 In which team event did John Panton compete internationally?

9 How many different clubs did Alex Ferguson play for?

10 In which year did Sam Torrance win the Spanish Open?

11 Which club did Alex Ferguson manage immediately before he joined Aberdeen?

12 Jessie Valentine made her name in which sport?

13 At which weight did Donnie Hood win the WBC International title in 1990?

14 At which weight did Paul Weir win the world title in 1995?

15 Which two European titles has golfer Bernard Gallacher won?

ANSWERS

1. 3,838 2. Yvonne Murray 3. Eric Caldow 4. Lightweight 5. Dunfermline Athletic, in 1961 and 1968 6. Golf (Walker Cup) 7. Firs Park 8. Ryder Cup 9. Six - Queen's Park, St Johnstone, Dunfermline, Rangers, Falkirk and Ayr United 10. 1982 11. St Mirren 12. Golf 13. Bantamweight 14. Mini flyweight 15. Spanish Open and French Open

PEOPLE

1 David Peebles, a 16th-century composer, was a canon; where?

2 August Monns conducted which orchestra for many years?

3 Why was Sir Andrew Wood granted lands in Largo in 1489?

4 What was Wood's famous ship?

5 What alteration did Wood make to his new estate, in keeping with his nautical background?

6 Whose first painting *Pitlessie Fair* brought him fame at the age of 19?

7 The robbing of exciseman James Stark in Pittenween eventually led to which famous riots in Edinburgh?

8 Which archbishop was murdered at Magus Muir by aggrieved Covenanters in 1679?

9 Bishop Henry Wardlaw was instrumental in the founding of which seat of higher learning?

10 In which year did he found it?

11 Which 17th-century writer produced the first topography of Scotland?

12 With which instrument was the 16th-century musician Sir John Futhy of Aberdeen associated?

13 At which musical instrument did James I particualrly excel?

14 Marjory Kennedy-Fraser spent a life's work collecting songs from where?

15 Which Chancellor of Scotland added St Salvator's College to St Andrews University?

ANSWERS

1. St Andrews 2. Choral Union, Edinburgh 3. He defeated an English squadron in the Forth of Fife 4. The *Yellow Carvel* 5. He had a canal built so that he could be rowed to church 6. Sir David Wilkie 7. Porteous Riot 8. Archbishop Sharp 9. St Andrews University 10. 1411 11. Sir John Scott 12. Organ 13. Harp 14. The Hebrides 15. Bishop James Kennedy

1 *More Songs of Angus* is a collection of which poet's work?

2 Who wrote the 1932 novel *Mungo?*

3 'White-maa' is the Orcadian term for which bird?

4 John Brandane was the open-name of which playwright?

5 Who wrote the novel *Highland River?*

6 The poet Gavin Douglas held which ecclesiastical post?

7 In which Scott novel would you encounter the aged minstrel Bertram?

8 Who wrote *The Brownie of Bodsbeck?*

9 Who wrote the novel *Cottages of Glenburnie?*

10 What does 'aiblin' mean in Burns's poetry?

11 Who wrote introductions to his novels under the name Jedediah Cleishbotham?

12 James Bridie was the pen-name of which playwright?

13 *A Humble Remonstrance,* an essay by Robert Louis Stevenson, was written response to an essay by whom?

14 Joseph Bell, an Edinburgh medicine instructor, was the inspiration for which famous detective?

15 In which Scott novel would you the young farmer Hobbie Elliot?

ANSWERS

1. Violet Jacob 2. George Woden 3. Herring gull 4. John MacIntyre 5. Neil Gunn 6. Bishop of Dunkeld 7. *Castle Dangerous* 8. James Hogg 9. Elizabeth Hamilton 10. Perhaps 11. John Galt 12. Dr O H Mavor 13. Henry James 14. Sherlock Holmes 15. *The Black Dwarf*

157

GENERAL KNOWLEDGE

1   Which British Prime Minister was born in Whittinghame House, near East Linton, Lothian?

2   Who said that Edinburgh was a city 'that no place in the world can compete with'?

3   Which famous cannon was used at the Siege of Norham?

4   Which writers, known as the 'Three Roberts', were commemorated by the Saltire Society with a plaque in Edinburgh's Cannongate Church in 1988?

5   In which field did the poet Allan Ramsay's son, also Allan, distinguish himself?

6   Which vegetable was introduced to Britain by Patrick Miller in the 18th century?

7   Which was the first Scottish Safari Park?

8   In which year did it open?

9   James Smith (1789-1850) is credited with developing which agricultural implement?

10   John Moir of Aberdeen is credited with being the first to can which food in 1825?

11   Britain's first military campaign medal, instituted in 1650, takes its name from which battle?

12   In 1812, James and Patrick Clark became the first people to use cotton to make what?

13   Which is the oldest Highland regiment?

14   In which year was it founded?

15   Which Scottish naturalist founded Kew Gardens in London?

ANSWERS

1. A J Balfour 2. US President Thomas Jefferson 3. Mons Meg 4. Fergusson, Burns and Stevenson 5. Painting 6. swede 7. Blair Drummond 8. 1970 9. The subsoil plough 10. Salmon 11. Dunbar 12. Thread 13. The Black Watch 14. 1739 15. William Hooker

1 Which city is the most frequent winner of the Britain in Bloom competition?

2 Which is the largest house in Scotland?

3 Within 50 feet, how long is the west facade of this house?

4 Which is the most remote pub on the mainland of the UK?

5 Where is the UK's oldest working post office?

6 Where are the highest cliffs in Britain?

7 Which place, apart from Kirkcaldy, is often nicknamed the Lang Toun?

8 What is unusual about Compass Hill on the island of Canna?

9 Where is McCaig's Folly?

10 Which is the Queen of the South?

11 Where is the oldest habitation so far found in Scotland?

12 Which village has the steepest access road in the UK?

13 Which town is known as the Capital of the Highlands?

14 Where was the largest meteorite in Scotland found, in 1917?

15 Within 5 pounds, how much did it weigh?

ANSWERS

1. Aberdeen 2. Hopetoun House, West Lothian 3. 675 ft/206 m 4. Old Forge Pub, Inverie, Knoydart (7-mile/11 km sail or 18-mile/29 km trek) 5. Sanquhar, near Dumfries 6. Conachair Cliffs, St Kilda 7. Auchterarder, Perthshire 8. Its basaltic rocks contain a high proportion of iron ore, which affects ships' compasses 9. Oban 10. Dumfries 11. Jura: a hearth from the Mesolithic period (8,000 years old) 12. Applecross 13. Inverness 14. Strathmore, Tayside 15. 22.25 lbs/10 kg

HISTORY

to Proof

1 How many children did James VI (James I of England) have?

2 Who joined forces with the English Lord Dacre to defeat reivers at the Raid of Eskdale in 1504?

3 Whose embalmed head did Queen Elizabeth I's master glazier use as a potpourri?

4 In which year did the Douglases beat the Hamiltons in a bloody battle on Edinburgh's High Street?

5 How did Sir James Douglas recapture his castle from the English in 1307?

6 What nickname did this incident earn?

7 In which century was Dumbarton Rock first fortified?

8 How did a 1471 charter define the fee for the hereditary keepership of Dunoon Castle?

9 Which native of the area East Kilbride was considered to be the 'Mata Hari of the '45'?

10 What happened at the 'Battle of Carlochhead'?

11 Which king founded the University of Glasgow?

12 Which religious community was founded by Rev George MacLeod?

13 In which year did Montrose win the Battle of Kilsyth?

14 In which year did the Pictish Saint Moluag evangelise Lisomre?

15 Which king was defeated at the Battle of the Standard and died in Carlisle in 1153?

ANSWERS

1. Seven 2. James IV 3. James IV 4. 1520 5. He trapped them inside the church while they were worshipping on Palm Sunday 6. The Douglas Larder 7. The fifth 8. One red rose when asked for 9. Mrs Jeannie Cameron 10. Sir James Colquhon failed to stop a group of steamship trippers from landing on his shore 11. James II 12. The Iona Community 13. 1645 14. Sixth 15. David I

1 The last what was killed in Lothian in 1700?

2 What occurred at Dryburgh Abbey in 1975 for the first time in three centuries?

3 Thomas of Ercildoune and True Thomas are alternatives of whose name?

4 The 'Cleikun ceremony' celebrates the miraculous feats of which saint?

5 Which 'jingling Geordie' founded a famous Edinburgh school?

6 What is Argyll's Bowling Green?

7 What was the 'Cambuslang Wark'?

8 What was the only Jacobite banner not to be burnt by the Common Hangman at Edinburgh in 1746?

9 Whittinghame is associated with the introduction of what article of agricultural machinery to Scotland?

10 In which century did Saint Baldred die?

11 In which year was the first Red Hose Race run?

12 How is Colmonell pronounced?

13 Which prominent Jacobite was later dubbed 'the Mata Hari of the '45'?

14 In which shipyard was the *Aquitania* dismantled?

15 Near which island is tiny Council Island?

ANSWERS

1. Wolf 2. A Catholic Mass was celebrated 3. Thomas the Rhymer 4. Ronan 5. George Heriot 6. A peninsula between Lochs Goil and Long 7. A religious festival of 1742 8. The Appin Colours 9. Combine harvester 10. Eighth 11. 1500 12. Com-mon-ell 13. Jeannie Cameron 14. Faslane 15. Eilean Mor

TV & ENTERTAINMENT

1   Which was the last Bay City Rollers song to reach the charts, in 1977?

2   Who directed the 1948 film version of *Macbeth*?

3   Neil Christian had one chart hit, in 1966. Which song was it?

4   In which year did TV's 'Madame Sin' screen?

5   What connects a Boston sports bar with Nessie?

6   Which 1996 film version of a classic American TV thriller was filmed partly in Scotland?

7   In which 1987 film does Sean Connery play a Prohibition-era G-man in Chicago?

8   Which 1983 film by Monty Python used Scottish location shots?

9   Which group took 'Party Fears Two' to number 9 in the charts in 1982?

10 Who directed *My Name is Joe* (1998)?

11 Who had a hit in 1980 with 'January February'?

12 In which year was *The Prime of Miss Jean Brodie* released?

13 Which comedian starred in the 1977 film *Big Banana Feet*?

14 Which 1936 documentary film featured a screenplay by W H Auden?

15 Which group took 'Love is a Stranger' to number 6 in the charts in 1983?

ANSWERS

1. 'You Made Me Believe in Magic' 2. Orson Welles 3. 'That's Nice' 4. 1972 5. Ted Danson: star of 'Cheers' and the film Loch Ness 6. Mission Impossible 7. The Untouchables 8. The Meaning of Life 9. Associates 10. Ken Loach 11. Barbara Dickson 12. 1969 13. Billy Connolly 14. Night Mail 15. Eurythmics

1 Which Scottish runner won the 200-metre gold at the 1998 European Championships?

2 At which weight did Paul Weir win the European title in 1996?

3 Who scored a hat-trick for Hearts in the 1956 Scottish Cup Final against Motherwell?

4 Which is the only Grand Slam title that Tommy Armour never held?

5 What is the name of Kilmarnock's ground?

6 In which year did Sandy Lyle win the Open?

7 Who plays at Links Park?

8 Who became Aberdeen's youngest ever captain at 20 in 1970?

9 How old was Isabella Robertson when she won the British Ladies Open Amateur Golf Championship in 1981?

10 Which is the only English team in the Scottish League?

11 How many times has Willie Carson been Champion Jockey?

12 At which weight did Willie Quinn win the WBO Intercontinental title in 1995?

13 Which goalkeeper was Morton's most capped international player with 25 appearances for Scotland?

14 Which international title did Ronnie Shade win in 1966?

15 In which year did the Scottish horse Rubstick win the Grand National?

ANSWERS

1. Dougie Walker 2. Light flyweight 3. Willie Bauld 4. Masters 5. Rugby Park 6. 1985 7. Montrose 8. Martin Buchan 9. 45 10. Berwick Rangers 11. five 12. Middleweight 13. Jimmy Cowan 14. World Amateur Golf Championship 15. 1979

PEOPLE

1 Whose arrest is closely linked to the Porteous Riots in Edinburgh?

2 In which Scott novel is their story told?

3 Who founded the library of St Andrews University?

4 Edward Kellie held which position in the court of Charles I?

5 Why was a heavy door, laden with boulders, put on Pittenweem native Janet Cornfrost in 1705?

6 What is another name for St Monans?

7 Who designed St George's Church, Glasgow?

8 Which Edinburgh architect oversaw much of London's Georgian redevelopment?

9 How long did Andrew Bonar-Law serve as Prime Minister?

10 Whom did he join in a wartime coalition?

11 In which year did Sir Arthur Conan Doye die?

12 Who designed the Scottish National Portrait Gallery?

13 Which Air Chief Mashall was a spriritualist and believed to be in communication with fallen airmen?

14 Who is considered to be the 'father of sociology'?

15 Which famous Scottish electronics engineer took a patent out on fibre optics?

ANSWERS

1. Andrew Wilson and his colleague Robertson 2. *Heart of Midlothian* 3. James VI 4. Director of Music 5. As a sentence for her witchcraft conviction 6. St Mirren 7. Robert Stark 8. Robert Adam 9. One year 10. Lloyd George 11. 1930 12. Sir Rowand Anderson 13. Hugh Dowding 14. Adam Ferguson 15. John Logie Baird

1 *Europe* is the work of which young Scottish dramatist?

2 In which country is Scott's *Quentin Durward* set?

3 In which year was *Peter Pan* published?

4 What is the setting of Scott's novel *The Pirate?*

5 Who wrote the novel and play *The Little Minister?*

6 Which Scott poem has the lines 'O Caledonia stern and wild/Meet nurse for a poetic child'?

7 The Jacobite song 'Hey Johnny Cope' celebrates which victory?

8 Which literary figure nearly lost his life in the Linn of Dee ravine?

9 Which glen is famed for the purity of the Gaelic spoken there?

10 Which battle of 1396 features in Scott's *The Fair Maid of Perth?*

11 Who wrote the successful history *Culloden* in 1961?

12 In which Scott novel would you Alan Fairford?

13 A long poem describing which grisly event is usually attributed to Murdoch Matheson?

14 Which founder member of the Royal Society was James II's chief minister in Scotland?

15 Whose mother keeps the Admiral Benbow Inn?

ANSWERS

GENERAL KNOWLEDGE

1   Which university founded the first chair of agriculture in Britain?

2   Where does the Bruichladdich Islands Peak Race begin?

3   Where does the Bruichladdich Islands Peak Race end?

4   On which three islands do competitors in the Bruichladdich Islands Peak Race stop for runs?

5   Which Scottish agronomist first applied modern chemical principles to agriculture?

6   The 71st Highland Light Infantry is famous for having fired the last shot at which battle?

7   Which is the oldest Scots infantry regiment in the British Army?

8   In which year was this regiment founded?

9   How much did a 60-year-old bottle of The Macallan fetch when it was sold by the Rotary Club of Elgin in 1988?

10   What is Cullen Skink?

11   How many gallons did the world's largest bottle of whisky, of William Grant Reserve Finest Scotch Whisky, contain?

12   How many people died in the German bombing raid on Clydeside on March 13-14, 1941?

13   Who pioneered the use of steam in agriculture?

14   Which region has the largest concentration of whisky distilleries?

15   What type of geographical feature is An Steall Ban?

ANSWERS

1. Edinburgh 2. Oban 3. Troon 4. Mull, Jura and Arran 5. Frances Home 6. Waterloo 7. Royal Scots 8. 1535 9. £6,000 10. smoked haddock soup with potatoes, onions and milk 11. 41 12. 1,200 13. William Harley 14. Speyside 15. waterfall

1 On which island is Duntulm Castle?

2 Which is the most northerly habitation in Scotland?

3 What construction record does the Bell Sports Centre, Perth, hold?

4 What is unusual about the Little Japanese Delicatessen, Edinburgh?

5 Aberdeen can claim which Norwegian composers as one of its 'sons'?

6 Floors Castle was used as a setting for scenes in which film concerning Africa?

7 Which castle inspired Bram Stoker's *Dracula*?

8 Where are the longest stairs in the UK?

9 What was unusual about Angus Macaskill, born in Dunvega, Skye in 1823?

10 What is unusual about the Puff Inn, St Kilda?

11 The village of Haddington has a museum devoted to which individual?

12 Which castle is near the geological oddity known as the Electric Brae?

13 Which is the UK's highest restaurant?

14 Within 250 feet, how high above sea level is this restaurant?

15 What record does the Horsehoe pub, Drury Street, Glasgow, hold?

ANSWERS

1. Skye 2. Muckle Flugga lighthouse 3. The largest dome in the UK 222 ft/68 m in diameter 4. It is Scotland's only Japanese take-away 5. Edvard Grieg his father was Aberdonian 6. *Greystoke, the Legend of Tarzan, Lord of the Apes* 7. Slains Castle 8. Cruachan Power Station (1,065 ft/325 m) 9. He was the tallest non-pathological giant (7 feet, 9 inches/2.36 m) 10. It is Scotland's most westerly bar 11. Jane Welsh Carlyle 12. Culzean 13. The Ptarmigan Observation Restaurant, Cairngorm 14. 3,650 ft/1113 m 15. it has the longest bar in a UK pub (104 ft/32 m)

HISTORY

1 Which Scottish king married Sibylla, daughter of Henry I of England?

2 In which year was the first steamship built on the Clyde?

3 In which century, and by whom, was the first documented sighting of the Loch Ness Monster?

4 How many times did James VII (James II of England) marry?

5 What was the name of his first wife?

6 In which year was the Free Church of Scotland founded?

7 What term describes this event?

8 Which king was killed by the Danes at Crail in AD874?

9 Which king had the nickname 'the Fierce'?

10 Who was the mother of Mary, Queen of Scots?

11 In which year did the last recognised duel take place in Scotland?

12 Who, in Linlithgow, warned James IV about impending defeat at Flodden?

13 What was the name of the ascetic branch of the Benedictines who built three abbeys in Scotland in the Middle Ages?

14 Which saint is credited with having raised Saint Mungo?

15 Which king was placed on the throne by the English army in 1097?

ANSWERS

1. Alexander I 2. 1801 3. The 6th-Century, by Saint Columba 4. Twice 5. Anne Hyde 6. 1843 7. The Disruption 8. Constantine 9. Alexander I 10. Mary of Guise 11. 1822 12. A ghost 13. The Valliscaulians 14. Saint Serf 15. Edgar

TRIVIA

1. Whom did the 14 councillors of Council Island advise when they were summoned there?

2. In what year was the 'Battle of Garelochhead'?

3. Around which stone would Gourock couples circle to get 'Granny's blessing'?

4. Why was Inverary parish church designed with a dividing wall?

5. What title did Sir Alec Douglas Home take?

6. What is the only Scottish region to consist wholly of its former county?

7. Where is Macduff's Cross?

8. What does the 'ween' in Pittenween mean?

9. What murderous event took place at Magus Muir in 1679?

10. The present Prince of Wales assumed his first naval command at Rosyth; in which year?

11. What was his rank upon assuming command?

12. What was the name of the Prince's vessel?

13. What colour are the traditional robes of St Andrews students?

14. Which Archbishop of St Andrews and Edinburgh was created Cardinal in 1969?

15. Who invented the reflector telescope?

ANSWERS

1. The Lord of the Isles 2. 1853 3. Granny Kempock's Stone 4. So that services could proceed in English and Gaelic 5. Lord Home of The Hirsel 6. Fife 7. Newburgh 8. Cave 9. Archbishop Sharp was murdered by Covenanters 10. 1976 11. Lieutenant 12. HMS *Bronington* 13. Scarlet 14. Gordon Gray 15. James Gregory

TV & ENTERTAINMENT

1 Which group got a popular response to their number 8 hit 'Rip it Up' in 1983?

2 Which Scottish actress played a Pearl Harbour officer's wife in *From Here to Eternity*?

3 Which legendary Borders hero was commemorated in a 1995 blockbuster film?

4 Who starred in the title role of this film?

5 How high in the charts did 'Thorn in My Side', by the Eurythmics, go in 1986?

6 Pilot achieved number one status with their one chart hit in 1975. Its name?

7 Which singer was born in Bellshill on 27 Aril 1959?

8 Which is the only film that Sean Connery made with Alfred Hitchcock?

9 Which actress, a Hitchcock favourite, was his co-star?

10 Where is Tom Conti's birthplace?

11 How high did the Proclaimers' song 'Letter from America' climb in 1987?

12 Who took 'Chance' to number 9 in 1983?

13 Which brothers wrote Rod Stewart's smash hit 'Sailing'?

14 With which song from the musical *Hair* did Paul Jones have a chart hit in 1969?

15 Which Scottish group released a successful EP 'Four Bacharach and David Songs' in 1990?

ANSWERS

1. Orange Juice 2. Deborah Kerr 3. *Rob Roy* 4. Liam Neeson 5. number 5 6. 'January' 7. Sheen Easton 8. *Marnie* 9. Tippi Hedren 10. Paisley 11. Number 3 12. Big Country 13. The Sutherland Brothers 14. Aquarius 15. Deacon Blue

SPORT

1 From which Scottish club did Chelsea buy Charlie Cooke?

2 Which European club did John Collins leave Celtic to go to in 1996?

3 Which coveted title did Robert Millar win in the 1984 Tour de France?

4 How many teams are there in the Scottish Football League?

5 In which year did David Wilkie win an Olympic gold medal in swimming?

6 In which event did Wilkie win the gold?

7 In which sport has Rita Montgomery twice won veterans' road races?

8 How many times did Tommy Docherty play for Scotland?

9 Where is Britain's oldest real tennis court still in use?

10 Which record did 'Mormond Lad' set in 1977?

11 Who was the last amateur player to captain Scotland in football?

12 With a time of 2 hours, 58 minutes and 48 seconds, which record did Colin Simpkins set in 1987?

13 Which is Scotland's oldest angling club?

14 Which team plays at Somerset Park?

15 Within 30 miles, how long is the North of Scotland Inflatable Boats Race?

ANSWERS

1. Dundee 2. Monaco 3. King of the Mountains 4. 40, ten in each division 5. 1976 6. 200 metres breaststroke 7. Cycling 8. 25 9. Falkland Palace 10. Fastest record to the UK (pigeon-racing) 11. Bobby Gillespie 12. Fastest canoe trip along Loch Ness (Fort Augustus to Lochend) 13. Ellem Fishing Club 14. Ayr United 15. 545 miles/877 km

PEOPLE

1 Whose declaration of 1917 promised a Palestine homeland for Zionists?

2 In what year did Alexander Graham Bell invent the telephone?

3 Which Scots-born Secretary of State for Ireland told landowners that 'property has its duties as well as its rights'?

4 What was the name of his invention, used to help navigation?

5 In what year did Sir James Barrie die?

6 Who invented the penumatic tyre?

7 Who is often - and wrongly - assumed to have invented it?

8 James Braid was a pioneer in which psychological field?

9 What term, later shortened to its present form, did he use to describe this process?

10 Which Protestant reformer did Cardinal David Beaton execute in the same year as his own murder?

11 What is Sheena Easton's real name?

12 Which city in Australia is named after an Ayshire astronomer?

13 Of which Australian state did he become governor-general?

14 Which Aberdeen-born soldier and inventor died at the Battle of King's Mountain, South Carolina, in 1780?

15 Which Glasgow professor developed the concept of 'latent heat'?

ANSWERS

1. Arthur James Balfour 2. 1876 3. Thomas Drummond 4. The 'Drummond Light', in lighthouses 5. 1937 6. Robert William Thomson 7. John Boyd Dunlop 8. Hypnosis 9. Neurohypnosis 10. George Wishart 11. Sheena Orr 12. Brisbane, after Sir Thomas Makdougall Brisbane 13. New South Wales 14. Patrick Ferguson 15. Joseph Black

1 Which David Greig play deals with the life of 18th-century financier John Law?

2 What is the *Scotichronicon*?

3 Which Sir Walter Scott original manuscript is on display at Bowhill?

4 Wordsworth wrote a sonnet to 'Old Q'. Who was he?

5 Who is credited with writing the poem 'Peblis to the Play', concerning Peebles?

6 Who wrote 'The Pleasures of Hope'?

7 Which 19th-century novel begins with the murder of William Wellow's wife?

8 Who wrote *Thaddeus of Warsaw*?

9 Who wrote the poem 'Lochie's Warning'?

10 In which Scott novel would you encounter Jeanie and Effie Deans?

11 Who wrote the 1807 novel *The Hungarian Brothers*?

12 The events of *The Hungarian Brothers* concern which historical period?

13 *Airport* is a work of which Scottish dramatist?

14 Which 19th-century critic had a fierce reputation, earning him the nickname 'the Scorpion'?

15 In which Scott novel would you meet Grace Armstrong?

ANSWERS

1. *The Speculator* 2. A medieval history of Scotland 3. *Lay of the Last Minstrel* 4. The Fourth Duke of Queensberry 5. James VI 6. Thomas Campbell 7. *The Scottish Chiefs* 8. Jane Porter 9. Thomas Campbell 10. *Heart of Midlothian* 11. Anna Maria Porter 12. The French Revolution 13. David Greig 14. John Gibson Lockhart 15. *The Black Dwarf*

GENERAL KNOWLEDGE

1   Andrew Meikle developed which labour-saving agricultural device in the late 18th century?

2   What is another name for Tinnis Castle?

3   What was Thomas the Rhymer's real name?

4   What is the name of the annual mounted procession in Galashiels?

5   Which canal was built by John Rennie in 1793-1801?

6   The strongnolds near which Ayrshire town were once described here: 'Auld castles grey, nod to the moon'?

7   What was the first steamship built on the Clyde?

8   In which notorious Ayrshire fair would smugglers mingle with local shepherds and hill-folk?

9   The Valliscaulians were an ascetic branch of which religious order?

10 In which year did John Knox celebrate the first Holy Communion according to Presbyterian rites?

11 The 'Cleikuns ceremony' is part of which competition?

12 *Tyribus ye tyr ye Odin* is which town's song?

13 What sort of people were 'callants'?

14 In which year did B.O.A.C. begin flights from Prestiwck to New York?

15 What does 'strath' mean?

ANSWERS

1. Threshing machine 2. Thanes Castle 3. Sir Thomas Learmount 4. The Braw Lads Gathering 5. Crinan Canal 6. Colmonell 7. *Charlotte Dundas* 8. Kirkdandie Fair 9. Benedictines 10. 1556 11. Border Games 12. Hawick 13. Young people 14. 1946 15. Valley

PLACES

1 Which road from Darlington to Edinburgh traces the route of the ancient Roman road?

2 In which Glasgow square is there an equestrian statue of Queen Victoria?

3 Where is the Green Hill Covenanter's House?

4 Abbey Saint Bathan's lies along which river?

5 Luffness House stands by which Lothian village?

6 Renegade monks from which abbey were sent to Ailsa Crag in the Middle Ages?

7 Loudoun Hall is the oldest building in which town?

8 In which castle, now ruined, was Allan Stewart, commander of Corssraguel Abbey, roasted to death in 1570?

9 The woodland area of Glen App lies just outside which seaside town?

10 Which gruesome landmark is found at Benane Head, near Ballantrae?

11 Barrhead lies between which two rivers?

12 Which district of Glasgow has a large population of Lithuanian descent, people whose forebears had been captured in the Crimean War?

13 Which town crowns a Fleming Queen each July?

14 Bridge of Weir lies along which river?

15 Where has the Papingo Shoot, an archery competition, been held since 1488?

ANSWERS

1. The A68 2. George Square 3. Biggar 4. Whiteadder Water 5. Aberlady 6. Crossraguel Abbey 7. Ayr 8. Dunure 9. Ballantrae 10. Sawney Bean's Cave, a former den of cannibals 11. Levern and Kirkton 12. Bellshill 13. Biggar 14. Gryfewater 15. Kilwinning

HISTORY

1 What was the name of Macbeth's wife?

2 In which year did James Ramsay MacDonald lead the first Labour government?

3 Where did Malcolm III die in 1093?

4 Which Scottish queen was canonised in 1251?

5 Which king was assassinated in a privy in Perth?

6 In which year was the Scottish Orchestra formed?

7 Who was its first conductor?

8 Which 12th-century king established many religious houses across Scotland?

9 How many of the six Scottish kings named James had Scottish wives?

10 In which year did Dr William McEwan set up his Fountain Brewery in Edinburgh?

11 Which 11th-century king had his eyes put out and died in prison?

12 Who claimed Antarctica for Queen Victoria in 1841?

13 Where did Robert the Bruce die?

14 Which famous Scot was Minister of Works from 1940 to 1942?

15 In which year did Alexander I die?

ANSWERS

1. Gruoch 2. 1924 3. Alnwick 4. Queen Margaret 5. James I 6. 1893 7. George Henschel 8. David I 9. None 10. 1856 11. Donald Bane 12. Sir James Clark Ross 13. Cardross 14. Lord Reith 15. 1124

1 What are 'riggs'?

2 Who wrote *Between Ochills and the Firth* in 1888?

3 Does the place name Saline have anything to do with salt?

4 Which port's Festival of St Catherine once included a fair called the Haggis Market?

5 In which year did Parliament authorise the people of St Andrews to use the Cathedral for building stone?

6 To which other city was it proposed to move St Andrews University at about the same time?

7 Who wrote *Scot of Scotstarvit's Staggering State of Scots Statesmen?*

8 Why did the Black Watch regiment choose black as a colour?

9 What, in medieval times, was a Sang Scuil?

10 The 13th-century Wolfenbuttel Manuscript, compiled at St Andrews, comprises what?

11 When was The Musical Society founded in Edinburgh?

12 Which Edinburgh orchestra was founded in 1919?

13 What is another name for the musical term 'Scots Catch'?

14 Where is the UK's only gold-panning school?

15 What did 'Macmillan, the devil on wheels', do in 1840?

ANSWERS

1. Long gardens 2. David Beveridge 3. No - it comes from Sal Bhen, or 'big hill' 4. Newburgh 5. 1649 6. Perth 7. Sir John Scott (1585-1670) 8. To distinguish it from English Guardsmen or Red Soldiers 9. A musical school or academy 10. Church music 11. 1728 12. The Reid Symphony Orchestra 13. Scotch Snap 14. Wanlockhead, Dumfriesshire 15. Rode a pedal bicycle

TV & ENTERTAINMENT

1 Which Scottish actor appeared in both *Merry Christmas, Mr Lawrence* and *Reuben, Reuben?*

2 Who sang about the 'Boston Tea Party' in 1976?

3 Akira Kuroswa's *Throne of Blood* (1957) was a stylized Japanese version of which play?

4 Who was David McCallum's co-star in 'The Man from U.N.C.L.E.'?

5 Which 1994 film concerns a groom-to-be who wakes up naked in the Highlands after a wild stag night?

6 Which 1973 film concerns a policeman visiting a remote Scottish island and encountering a devil-worshipping cult?

7 Which famous playwright wrote the screenplay for this film?

8 Which 1956 film of a famous play uses rival gangsters instead of warring princes?

9 Who sang 'A Girl Like You', which was a 1994 chart hit?

10 Who directed the 1979 film *That Sinking Feeling?*

11 What was the unusual name of the Cocteau Twins' number 29 hit in 1984?

12 Which group took 'Look Away' to number 7 in the charts in 1986?

13 Which Scottish comedian once worked as an oil-rig welder in Biafra?

14 Who played Dr. Janet Napier in the'Taggart episode 'Fatal Inheritance'?

15 What role did David McCallum play in the TV version of 'Cluedo'?

ANSWERS

1 With a distance of 51.596 km, which title did Graeme Obree win in 1993?

2 Which is Scotland's oldest archery club?

3 Which Rangers player was Scottish Footballer of the Year twice, in 1976 and 1986?

4 In which event did Alan Pattirgrew achieve a record-breaking distance of 180 feet, 10 inches at Inchmurin, Loch Lomond, in 1984?

5 The Italian alchemist John Damian made the first known attempt at which sport at Stirling Castle in 1507?

6 In which country was Richard Gough born?

7 Which is Scotland's oldest curling club?

8 In which year was this club founded (within 15 years)?

9 From which Scottish club did Andy Goram join Rangers in 1991?

10 Kenny Dalglish holds the record for Scottish caps - how many?

11 Which of the Gray brothers, Frank or Eddie, won the most Scottish caps?

12 With a time of 1 hours, 25 minutes and 34 seconds, which record did Kenneth Stewart set in 1987?

13 Whom did Stephen Hendry beat at the 1999 Embassy World Snooker Championship?

14 Which Scottish club reached the semi-finals of the European Cup in 1963?

15 Sergeant Ronald Alan 'Scotty' Milne has won which British title five times?

ANSWERS

1. The one-hour cycling record 2. The Society of Kilwinning Archers 3. John Greig 4. Haggis hurling 5. Hang-gliding 6. Sweden 7. Muthill, Tayside 8. 1739 9. Hibernian 10. 102 11. Frank won 32, Eddie 12. The Ben Nevis summit and return 13. Mark Williams 14. Dundee 15. Parachuting

PEOPLE

1 At which two universities was Sir David Brewster associated?

2 For which James Bond film did Sheena Easton sing the theme song?

3 In what year were the song and film released?

4 Who oversaw the defeat of Luftwaffe forces in the Battle of Britain?

5 Who invented the percussion cap, used in firearms?

6 For the construction of which famous railway was Sir Sandford Fleming the chief engineer?

7 Who carried out the peaceful annexation of the Punjab?

8 Which famous canal did he open?

9 Who won the Nobel Prize for Medicine in 1944?

10 Which process of metal casting did William Ged invent?

11 Whose law concerns the diffusion of gases?

12 Whose first work was *The Storm*, published in 1954?

13 Which Aberdeenshire merchant is often considered to be the model for Puccini's *Madame Butterfly*?

14 Who reached the magnetic South Pole first, in 1909?

15 How many years later did Amundsen and Scott reach the geographic South Pole?

ANSWERS

1. St Andrews and Edinburgh 2. *For Your Eyes Only* 3. 1981 4. Air Chief Marshall Hugh Dowding 5. Rev Alexander Forsyth 6. Canadian Pacific 7. James Andrew Broun-Lindsay 8. The Ganges Canal 9. Sir Alexander Fleming 10. The 'lost wax' method 11. Thomas Graham 12. George Mackay Brown 13. Thomas Blake Glover 14. Alistair Forbes-Mackay 15. Three

1   Which publisher became involved in a bankruptcy case that led to a debt of £114,000 that was paid off by Sir Walter Scott?

2   In which Scott novel would you encounter Elshie of the Mucklestanes?

3   In which novel would you encounter the blind pirate Pew?

4   Which medieval Scottish philosopher wrote 'Quaestiones subtilissimae' on the metaphysics of Aristotle?

5   Who wrote the novel *Greenmantle*?

6   A famous murder in Ardchattan, Strathclyde, features in which Sir Walter Scott novel?

7   John Howe, the writer of *Douglas,* was minister at which Lothian church?

8   Who wrote the novel *the Raiders*?

9   The Braes of Balquhidder are celebrated in an 18th-century ballad by whom?

10 Who wrote *Rab and His Friends?*

11 Craighill Rattray, a 17th-century mansion in Blairgowrie, inspired which work by Sir Walter Scott?

12 Which 18th-century poet was born in Bothwell, Strathclyde, in 1762?

13 To whom did Scott's minstrel address his last lay?

14 Who wrote the novel *Dancing Floor?*

15 Who was the 'Red Fox' of Glenure?

ANSWERS

1. James Ballantyne & Co 2. *The Black Dwarf* 3. *Treasure Island* 4. John Duns Scotus 5. John Buchan 6. *Kidnapped* 7. Athelstaneford 8. S R Crockett 9. Robert Tannahill 10. Dr John Brown 11. *Waverley* 12. Joanna Baillie 13. Anne, Duchess of Buccleuch 14. John Buchan 15. Colin Campbell in *Kidnapped*

22

1 Which flat, agricultural island long produced grain for Iona?

2 What is a 'muckle roup'?

3 How is Kilconquhar pronounced?

4 What does the 'kettle' of Kingskettle mean?

5 Which festival of Gaelic culture is organised by An Comunn Gaidhealach?

6 What is the 'Scotch Snap'?

7 What is the strathspey?

8 Which city was most famous for its Sang Scuil in the Middle Ages?

9 In which year was the Scottish National Academy founded?

10 Which school of music, founded in 1890, was expanded to become the Scottish National Academy ?

11 Which is the smallest Scottish region, in terms of area?

12 Which Edinburgh University building was paid for 'by the pint'?

13 To which constituency was Lord Reith elected as MP in 1940?

14 In which year did he become the first general-manager of the BBC?

15 What relation was the Young Pretender to James VII (James II of England)?

ANSWERS

1. Three 2. A big sale 3. Kinucker 4. Battle 5. Highland Mod 6. A musical term: a short note on the beat followed by a long note off the beat 7. A folk-dance 8. Aberdeen 9. 1930 10. Glasgow Athenaeum School of Music 11. Fife 12. McEwan Hall 13. Southampton 14. 1922 15. Grandson

1 In which Strathclyde village is there a grotto to Our Lady of Lourdes?

2 Caddon Water flows into which river?

3 Dalbeattie lies in the wooded valley of which river?

4 Where is Scotland's smallest distillery?

5 What distinction does Garvault Hotel, near Kilbrace, Sutherland, claim?

6 Which is Britain's largest maternity hospital?

7 Which is Britain's largest hospital?

8 How many staffed beds are there in this hospital?

9 Where was the first Second World War German fighter shot down?

10 Where is the world's largest New Year's Party?

11 On which island is Fingals' Cave?

12 In which glen is Ossian's Cave?

13 Which deep loch is Europe's second-deepest hollow?

14 Which natural landmark is sometimes called 'Paddy's Stone'?

15 Why does this nickname apply?

ANSWERS

Belfast and Glasgow
11. Staffa 12. Glencoe 13. Loch Morar 14. Ailsa Craig 15. Because it is halfway between
Shotts 8. 1,600 9. Over the Forth Bridge on October 16, 1939 10. Edinburgh's Hogmanay
hotel 6. Simpson Memorial Maternity Pavilion, Edinburgh 7. Hartwood Hospital, near
1. Carfin 2. Tweed 3. Edradour, near Pitlochry 4. Urrwater 5. To be Britain's most remote

183

HISTORY

1 Which king granted the first (and still existing) Scottish Charter?

2 Who nationalised the UK's mines in 1946?

3 What Cabinet position did he hold at the time?

4 What later Cabinet position did he hold?

5 Who founded the first botanical gardens in Edinburgh?

6 Of which historical figure did Sir Walter Scott write a famous biography?

7 In which year did the painter Allan Ramsay return to Edinburgh to help spread the city's reputation?

8 Which country's forces captured John Knox and other Protestants in 1547?

9 Where were they captured?

10 What sort of 'sentence' did Knox serve after his capture?

11 Which Lord of the Isles burnt Edingburgh in 1429?

12 In which battle was Donald, Lord of the Isles, defeated by an army of Lowlanders?

13 In which year did this battle take place?

14 Who was dismissed from Aberdeen University on a charge of heresy in the 19th century?

15 Matilda of Huntingdon was married to which Scottish king?

ANSWERS

1. Duncan II 2. Manny Shinwell 3. Minister of Fuel and Power 4. Secretary of State for Defence 5. Sir Robert Sibbald 6. Napoleon 7. 1738 8. France 9. St Andrews 10. Serving in the galleys 11. Alexander 12. Harlaw 13. 1411 14. William Robertson-Smith 15. David I

1 Where is the Byre Theatre?

2 What 'first' did Dalswinton Loch witness in 1780?

3 On which island was Alexander Selkirk put ashore in 1705?

4 Limekilns, near Rosyth, claims - against all evidence - to be the birthplace of which sport?

5 The will of General Reid (d. 1807) provided for a Professorship of what at Edinburgh University?

6 Who was British Prime Minister between 1902 and 1906?

7 What title did he later take?

8 What was James Boswell's profession?

9 How did Sir David Brewster believe the newly invented kaleidoscope could be used?

10 Who founded the Scottish Oceanographical Laboratory in 1907?

11 Which Scot was awarded the Nobel Peace Prize in 1947?

12 Of which UN organisation was he chairman?

13 What advice did William Spiers Bruce offer to fellow explorer Scott of the Antarctic ?

14 What did Joseph Black describe as 'fixed air'?

15 Which piece of agricultural machinery did Rev Patrick Bell invent?

ANSWERS

1. St Andrews 2. The world's first steamboat ride 3. Juan Fernandez 4. Curling 5. Music 6. Arthur James Balfour 7. First Earl of Balfour 8. Lawyer 9. To design carpets 10. William Spiers Bruce 11. Lord John Boyd-Orr 12. Food and Agriculture Organisation (FAO) 13. That Scott's supply dumps were too far apart for the mission to succeed 14. Carbon dioxide 15. The reaping machine, a forerunner of the combine harvester

TV & ENTERTAINMENT

1 In which 1955 film did Deborah Kerr star opposite Yul Bryner?

2 Which song by Lloyd Cole and the Commotions shares a title with a classic Hollywood film starring Ray Milland?

3 In which year did Roman Polanski direct a version of *Macbeth?*

4 Who played the title role in that film?

5 Which three Lonnie Donnegan songs reached number one?

6 What was Lena Martell's real name?

7 Who sang 'Catch the Wind' in 1965?

8 Mark Knopfler wrote the theme song to which Bill Forsyth film?

9 Who had a hit with 'So Cold the Night' in 1986?

10 Johnny Keating had a number 8 hit in 1962 with the theme from which television series?

11 Which Scottish actor co-starred in the TV series 'Sapphire and Steel'?

12 Who had a top ten hit with 'Heart on My Sleeve' in 1976?

13 The Sensational Alex Harvey Band had one top ten hit, in 1975. Its title?

14 Who reached number five with 'Hi Ho Silver' in 1986?

15 In which year did Fairground Attraction reach number one with 'Perfect'?

ANSWERS

1. *The King and I* 2. 'Lost Weekend' 3. 1971 4. Jon Finch 5. 'Cumberland Gap', 'Putting on the style' and 'My Old Man's a Dustman' 6. Ellen Thomson 7. Donovan 8. *Local Hero* 9. The Communards 10. 'Z Cars' 11. David McCallum 12. Gallacher and Lyle 13. 'Delilah' 14. Jim Diamond 15. 1988

1 Which record did Stephen Hendry set by winning the 1999 Embassy World Snooker Championship?

2 What is the name of the referee who was injured by a missile thrown from the stands at the Old Firm match in May 1999?

3 Which Scot left Tottenham shortly after they won the UEFA Cup in 1972 having scored over 100 goals for them?

4 Which course is the home of the Hon. Company of Edinburgh Golfers?

5 The same company had which course as its home until 1891?

6 Which was the first home of the Hon. Company of Edinburgh Golfers?

7 Which team were runners-up in the Scottish First Division for 4 out of 5 seasons between 1960 and 1964, finally winning in 1965 on goal average from Hearts?

8 What would noblemen practise on 'lang butts' in the Middle Ages?

9 When was the last of Celtic's run of 9 consecutive League championships?

10 Where is Schawpark golf course?

11 Which Manchester United manager signed Joe Jordan from Leeds in January 1978?

12 Which Robert Louis Stevenson title would seem appropriate for the golfing section of the public library?

13 Which defender left Celtic for Chelsea in 1974, and won the last of his 27 international caps in the draw against Yugoslavia in the 1974 World Cup Finals?

14 The Marquis of Ailsa helped found which championship golf course in 1907?

15 Who developed the 'Superman' position in cycling?

ANSWERS

PEOPLE

1 Which Edinburgh-born founding father of Canada was founder and editor of the *Toronto Globe?*

2 Who said 'Thou false thief; dost thou say Mass at ma lug'?

3 In which Edinburgh church did she utter those words?

4 Which Scottish explorer discovered Coats Land, Antarctica, in 1902-4?

5 Which fiddler is considered as the father of the strathspey?

6 Who is considered as the father of town planning?

7 What was this town planner's other field of expertise, in which he held a Dundee Professorship?

8 Who is recognised as the father of colloid chemistry?

9 The Hunterian Museum, Glasgow took its name from which 18th-century scientist?

10 Who was the oldest MSP elected in May 1999?

11 Which architect was the most noted proponent of the 'Scottish baronial' style?

12 Finlay Campbell, a Scottish anaesthetist, assisted at whose famous birth in July 1978?

13 Who presented 8000 works of art to the City of Glasgow in 1944?

14 Where are these now housed?

15 What was frustrating about James Bruce's announcement of his discovery of the source of the Blue Nile?

ANSWERS

1. George Brown 2. Jenny Geddes 3. St Giles 4. William Spiers Bruce 5. Niel Gow 6. Sir Patrick Geddes 7. Botany 8. Thomas Graham 9. William Hunter 10. Winnie Ewing 11. David Bryce 12. Louise Brown, the first test tube baby' 13. Sir William Burrell 14. Pollock Park 15. The French congratulated him but the English did not believe him

1 Whose play *The Cosmonaut's Last Message to The Woman He Once Loved in The Former Soviet Union* opened in 1999?

2 The compiling of which historical document was overseen by Walter Bower in the 1440s?

3 Who wrote the lines 'like angel-visits, few and far between'?

4 Who wrote the 1810 novel *The Scottish Chiefs*?

5 Who wrote the novel *Reginald Dalton*?

6 In which year was Sir Walter Scott created a baronet?

7 Squire Trelawny is a character in which Robert Louis Stevenson novel?

8 In which two novels would you meet David Balfour?

9 Who wrote the novel *Mr Standfast*?

10 In which Scott novel would you encounter Reuben Butler?

11 Who wrote the novel *Midwinter*?

12 Who wrote the novel *Some Passages in the Life of Adam Blair*?

13 In which Scott novel would you encounter John Balfour of Burley?

14 In which novel would you encounter Ben Gunn?

15 James Stewart of the Glens appears in which novel?

ANSWERS

1. David Greig 2. the *Scotichronicon* 3. Thomas Campbell 4. Jane Porter 5. John Gibson Lockhart 6. 1820 7. *Treasure Island* 8. *Kidnapped* and *Catriona* 9. John Buchan 10. *Heart of Midlothian* 11. John Buchan 12. John Gibson Lockhart 13. *Castle Dangerous* 14. *Treasure Island* 15. *Catriona*

GENERAL KNOWLEDGE

1   The Crinan Canal ends at Crinan; where does it begin?

2   Within ten miles, how long a sea voyage does the Crinan Canal save?

3   With which musical instrument was William Marshall associated?

4   Which family had a unbroken run of 126 years holding the Chair of Anatomy at the University of Edinburgh?

5   Where was David Niven born?

6   Mungo Park died trying to find the source of which African river?

7   Who was the Queen Mother's father?

8   Who built the London and East India Docks?

9   Which country's patron saint is said to have been born by the River Clyde?

10   What was the Darien Farce?

11   Where is the best collection of portraits by Sir Henry Raeburn?

12   Which 19th-century headmaster of the Old School of Edinburgh was an early advocate of compulsory education?

13   Whose career took him from the Gorbals to become the world's leading investigator?

14   Which Scot holds the land speed record?

15   What is the record speed?

ANSWERS

1. Ardrishaig in Loch Fyne 2. 130 miles 3. Jew's Harp 4. Monro 5. Kirriemuir 6. Niger 7. The Earl of Strathmore 8. John Rennie 9. Ireland: Saint Patrick 10. An ill-fated plan to set up a Scottish trading colony in Central America 11. Edinburgh University 12. James Pillans 13. Allan Pinkerton 14. Richard Noble 15. 763 mph

PLACES

1   On which island is Sleat?

2   Where is Machrihanish Airport?

3   Which is the tallest of the Cairngorms?

4   Which is the only inland body of water not called a loch in Scotland?

5   Ancestors of which US President are buried in St Bride churchyard near which town?

6   Where, according to tradition, did King Malcom Canmore bestow surnames on the Scottish nobility?

7   The Soldier's Leap lies by which Jacobite battlefield?

8   What is Schihallion?

9   Lochgoilhead lies at the head of a branch of which loch?

10   Broomielaw is a continuation of which Glasgow street?

11   On which island is Scalasaig?

12   Ben-y-Vrackie rises just east of which resort?

13   Lamlash is a port on which island?

14   Which two A roads run through Islay?

15   What is the English for Rudha Rhobhaneis?

ANSWERS

1. Skye 2. Kintyre 3. Ben Macdhu 4. Lake of Menteith 5. McKinley 6. Forfar 7. Killiecrankie 8. A Perthshire mountain 9. Loch Long 10. Clyde Street 11. Colonsay 12. Pitlochry 13. Arran 14. A847 and A846 15. Butt of Lewis

HISTORY

1 Where was Saint Margaret buried?

2 Where was Sir Walter Scott buried in 1832?

3 What happened to the medieval scholar John Duns Scotus in 1991?

4 In which year was *Robinson Crusoe* published, bringing fame indirectly to Alexander Selkirk?

5 Who defeated Ramsay Macdonald in Seaham Harbour in 1935?

6 In which year did Lady Elizabeth Bowes-Lyon marry the Duke of York?

7 In which year was Kilchurn Castle built?

8 What relation was Lulach, the 'Simpleton king', to Macbeth?

9 Who translated 'The First Helvetic Confession' into Scots in 1536?

10 Which were the only two sacraments that this Protestant document recognised?

11 The year 1452 saw the death of which famous Earl?

12 The Battle of Blair-na-Parc took place in which year?

13 The Battle of Druimnacoub took place in which year?

14 In which year did James II accede to the Throne?

15 Ermengarde de Beaumont was married to which Scottish king?

ANSWERS

1. Dunfermline Abbey 2. The ruins of Dryburgh Abbey 3. He was elevated to the status of 'venerable' (first step to sainthood) by the Vatican 4. 1719 5. Manny Shinwell 6. 1923 7. 1440 8. Step-son 9. George Wishart 10. Baptism and Holy Communion 11. Earl of Douglas 12. 1466 13. 1429 14. 1437 15. William I (the Lion)

To Proof

1 Where could you find the Lead-Mining Museum?

2 Which Hollywood actor, who appeared in more than 400 films, is sometimes called 'Scotland's forgotten actor'?

3 How did David Douglas, after whom the Douglas fir is named, die?

4 Which Ayshire astronomer is remembered for his star catalogue of more than 7000 stars?

5 Which Glasgow-born American earned the nickname 'Grandfather of the United States'?

6 Which type of firearm was invented by Patrick Ferguson of Pitfour, Aberdeenshire?

7 In which battle was this weapon instrumental in securing a victory over American forces in 1777?

8 Who was the first 'jockey to the Queen'?

9 In which year did this jockey acquire that 'title'?

10 Who designed Fettes College?

11 Name the author: he graduated in medicine from Edinburgh University before practising there and then on-board ship and in the Boer War.

12 Which singer's career was boosted by a BBC documentary about how EMI manufactured a 'star' from an unknown?

13 Who was the 'Tartan Pimpernel' during the Second World War?

14 Sir William Fairbairn developed what material as a construction material?

15 Which castle is famous for its Bottle Dungeon?

ANSWERS

1. Wanlockhead, Dumfriesshire 2. Donald Crisp 3. From injuries received from a bull after falling into a bull pit in Hawaii 4. Sir Thomas MacDougall Brisbane 5. Robert Dinwiddie, after recognising George Washington's talents in Virginia 6. The breech-loading rifle 7. The Battle of Brandywine 8. Willie Carson 9. 1977 10. David Bryce 11. Arthur Conan Doyle 12. Sheena Easton 13. Donald Caskie 14. Tubular steel 15. St Andrews

TV & ENTERTAINMENT

1   Who had a 1958 hit singing about the 'Purple People Eater'?

2   Which Scottish singer was voted best new artist in 1981?

3   Deborah Kerr starred in which 1964 film adaptation of a Tennessee Williams play?

4   Who had a 1979 number five hit with 'Night Owl'?

5   Which of Lulu's hits went highest in the charts?

6   What is Lulu's real name?

7   Which world number one did Midge Ure co-write in 1984?

8   Have Jesus and Mary Chain ever had a top ten hit?

9   Which Thomas Hardy film adaptation of 1996 used Scottish locations?

10 Where was Ian Anderson born?

11 Who had a number 17 hit with 'Top of the Pops' in 1978?

12 What was the highest-placed hit for Jethro Tull?

13 In which year did it get released?

14 For his role in which film did Tom Conti receive an Academy Award nomination?

15 'Hoots Mon' was a number one hit for which group in 1958?

ANSWERS

1. Jackie Dennis 2. Sheena Easton 3. *Night of the Iguana* 5. 'Boom bang-a-bang' (number 2 in 1968) 6. Marie McDonald Lawrie 7. 'Do They Know It's Christmas?' 8. Yes, with 'April skies' (number 8 in 1987) 9. *Jude* 10. Dunfermline 11. The Rezillos 12. 'Living in the Past' (number 3) 13. 1969 14. *Reuben Reuben* 15. Lord Rockingham's XI

SPORT

1 In which year did Stephen Hendry come from 14-8 behind to beat Jimmy White 18-14 at the Embassy World Snooker Championship?

2 Which golf course formerly offered a prize of 'a cree and shawl' to the best player among local fishwives?

3 Which player, playing for Dundee reserves at the time, after being fouled by one of a pair of twins on the opposing side, is supposed to have punched both of them to make sure he got the right one?

4 What is the most popular team sport in Hawick?

5 What was the title of the Scottish World Cup Squad's 1974 hit?

6 Where is Scotland's oldest curling club?

7 Which club did Alex McLeish join as player-manager when he left Aberdeen after 16 years in 1994?

8 Why did golfers once change at Leuchars Junction?

9 Which Scot is credited with having developed cricket?

10 Where did he do this?

11 Which football team is nicknamed The Wasps?

12 Which sport was inaugurated in Scotland by the Scottish Council of Physical Education at Dunnkeld in 1962?

13 Which Scottish all-rounder has presented England in cricket in the late 1990s?

14 On which loch would you find the popular angling village of Taynuilt?

15 Which competition has The Society of Kilwinning Archers contested since 1488?

ANSWERS

1. 1992 2. Musselburgh 3. Gordon Strachan 4. Rugby 5. 'Easy Easy' 6. Upper Nithsdale 7. Motherwell 8. To reach St Andrews by train 9. Richard Nairn 10. Hampshire 11. Alloa 12. Orienteering 13. Dougie Brown 14. Etive 15. The Papingo Shoot

PEOPLE

1   Of which university was Thomas Carlyle rector?

2   Whose writing was rooted in the Mearns (the country of Kincardineshire)?

3   What is this author's real name?

4   Which Scottish politician was Prime Minister between 1906 and 1908?

5   Of which party was he leader?

6   Which famous cattle thief and Jacobite guerrilla died in 1734?

7   By blending art nouveau and Scottish Celtic traditionalism, which Glasgow designer achieved international fame at the outset of the 20th century?

8   In which city did William McGonagall spend most of his life?

9   Who invented the blast oven?

10 How did this invention help the iron industry?

11 Where was Willie Carson born?

12 Which architect designed the McEwan Graduation Hall in Edinburgh?

13 Who set up the Fountain Brewery in Edinburgh in 1856?

14 Which Aberdeenshire scientist showed that malaria was carried by mosquito?

15 Which 19th-century pioneer of photography was also a renowned portrait and landscape painter?

ANSWERS

1. Edinburgh 2. Lewis Grassic Gibbon 3. James Leslie Mitchell 4. Sir Henry Campbell-Bannerman 5. Liberal 6. Rob Roy MacGregor 7. Charles Rennie Mackintosh 8. Dundee 9. James Beaumont Neilson 10. By reducing the amount of coal needed to produce iron 11. Stirling 12. Sir Rowand Anderson 13. Dr William McEwan 14. Sir Patrick Manson 15. David Octavius Hill

MUSIC & LITERATURE

1 Who wrote the novel *Matthew Wald?*

2 Which two sisters wrote a series of popular historical novels in the early 1800s?

3 Adam Breck is a character in which adventure novel?

4 Who wrote *Pavilion on the Links?*

5 Who wrote the poem *To Leven Water?*

6 Who described the grassy hills of Crawfordjohn as 'inhabited solitude' in 1803?

7 In which Scott novel would you meet the Quaker Joshua Geddes?

8 In which novel do the characters set off in the schooner *Hispaniola?*

9 Which 19th-century composer wrote the comic opera 'Robin Hood'?

10 Robert Louis Stevenson's *Memoir of an Islet* describes which lighthouse rocks?

11 Which Dundee poet has recently published the collection *God's Gift to Women?*

12 In which town did the Jolly Beggars rant in Poosie Nancy's?

13 Which Oban musician published *Collexion of Highland Vocal Airs?*

14 Who wrote *Pilgrim of Glencoe?*

15 In which Scott novel would you encounter Elshender the Recluse?

ANSWERS

1. John Gibson Lockhart 2. Anna Maria and Jane Porter 3. *Kidnapped* 4. Robert Louis Stevenson 5. Tobias Smollett 6. Dorothy Wordsworth 7. *Redgauntlet* 8. *Treasure Island* 9. George MacFarren 10. Dubh Artach 11. Don Paterson 12. Mauchline 13. Patrick Macdonald 14. Thomas Campbell 15. *The Black Dwarf*

GENERAL KNOWLEDGE

1 At 1150 feet, what is the highest village in the Scottish Highlands?

2 Whose statue is at the top of the column in George Square in Glasgow?

3 Which town on the River Lossie has a ruined cathedral?

4 Where is the administrative centre of the Argyll and Bute region?

5 What is the surface area in square miles of Loch Lomond?

6 What is the name of Edinburgh's main bus depot?

7 Which firth forms the northern border of Fife?

8 Which firth forms the southern border of Fife?

9 Which line of inland navigation extends from Inverness to Loch Eil?

10 Where is Arthur's Seat?

11 On which day of the year does Up-Helly Aa take place?

12 At which abbey can the words "King Robert the Bruce" be seen in stonework at the top of its tower?

13 In which region is Edinburgh?

14 Which road connects Dumfries and Stranraer?

15 Who discovered the element krypton?

ANSWERS

1. Tomintoul 2. Walter Scott 3. Elgin 4. Lochgilphead 5. 27 square miles 6. St Andrew's Square 7. Tay 8. Forth 9. Caledonian Canal 10. Holyrood Park 11. The last Tuesday in January 12. Dunfermline 13. Lothian 14. A75 15. Sir William Ramsay

PLACES

1 Colonsay is linked by ferry to which mainland town?

2 Which major airport lies just south of Troon?

3 Lochingar is part of which mountain range?

4 Where would you find St Enoch Station?

5 The site of the Roman camp of Grassy Walls is just north of which palace?

6 What are the highest peaks on Jura?

7 Lewis Grassie Gibbon wrote of the 'shining mail' of which city?

8 Where did Montrose score a remarkable victory in 1644, allowing him to enter Perth?

9 The Gulf of Corryvechan separates which two islands?

10 Tarbert is linked by ferry to which port on Skye?

11 Which town lies 12 miles north of Hawick on the A73?

12 Ben Lawers towers over which loch?

13 Which two A roads meet at John o' Groats?

14 Which port lies due south of Dornoch across Dornoch Firth?

15 On which island is the seaside village of Glenbrittle House?

ANSWERS

1. Oban 2. Prestwick 3. Grampians 4. Glasgow 5. Scone 6. The Paps of Jura 7. Aberdeen 8. Tibbermore 9. Jura and Scarba 10. Vig 11. Selkirk 12. Loch Tay 13. A836 and A99 14. Tain 15. Skye

HISTORY

1   Who were the 'assured Scots' of the 16th century?

2   What name was given to the Protestant Lords of Kincardineshire in the 16th century?

3   In which year did the English defeat the Scots at the Battle of Homildon Hill?

4   In which year was Bonnie Dundee's Revolt?

5   Which 16th-century negotiatior earned the nickname 'Michael Wylie' *Machiavelli* because of his subtlety?

6   In which year did the Darien Expedition take place?

7   Which English company were the Scots aiming to emulate in this venture?

8   In which year is Scotland's patron saint, Andrew, believed to have died?

9   In what year did Kirkcaldy begin its linoleum industry?

10   In which year did John Knox return to Scotland permanently after his exile in Europe and England?

11   The 'Master of the Stair' was gave the orders for which atrocity of 1692?

12   Who, in turn, gave him his orders?

13   Which English soldier defeated the Scots at the Battle of Otterburn?

14   Who re-founded the Abbey of Iona in the 11th century?

15   Which Scottish king was a hostage of William the Conqueror?

ANSWERS

1 Who oversaw the famous 'Dambusters Raid' of 1943?

2 Which top-ranking private school was founded for the benefit of poor and orphaned children?

3 In which year was the school founded?

4 Which two beverages provided the basis for its founder's fortune?

5 Who invented the 'lost wax' method of metal casting?

6 In which year was Sir Alexander Fleming, discoverer of penicillin, knighted?

7 What was Jenny Geddes famous for throwing at the Bishop in St Giles Church, Edinburgh?

8 Why did she do this?

9 What geographical landmark did Alistair Forbes-Mackay reach in 1909?

10 As part of whose expedition was he a member when he did this?

11 What was the name of the new-town experiment in social engineering created by David Dale in 1785?

12 Who is linked with the song 'I belong to Glasgow'?

13 The brothers Archibald and James Geikie were leaders in which branch of sicence?

14 Who was chief engineer in the construction of the Canadian Pacific Railway?

15 Where is Kennedy's Mace carried?

ANSWERS

1. Sir Ralph Alexander Cochrane 2. Fettes College 3. 1870 4. Tea and wine 5. William Ged 6. 1944 7. A stool 8. In protest at the 'Catholic' nature of the English prayerbook 9. The magnetic South Pole 10. Ernest Shackleton 11. New Lanark 12. Will Fyfe 13. Geology 14. Sir Sandford Fleming 15. At official functions of St Andrews University

TV & ENTERTAINMENT

1 Which Sheena Easton hit was renamed 'Morning Train' in the United States?

2 How high did its British version reach in the charts?

3 In which US city was film director Alexander Mackendrick born?

4 The father of which film director was a Scottish-born Prime Minister?

5 For which film did David Niven receive an Academy Award for Best Actor?

6 For his performance in which film did Sean Connery win an Oscar in 1987?

7 Which Scottish actor starred in the TV version of 'The Invisible Man' (1975)?

8 The 1969 film *Language* was whose first film as director?

9 Which versatile Scottish actor began his career in 1942 with *The Foreman Went to France*?

10 In which year did Deborah Kerr receive an honourary Academy Award?

11 Who had a hit with 'So Cold the Night' in 1986?

12 What was the only number one hit for Wet Wet Wet?

13 In which 1962 film about the D-Day invasion did Sean Connery have a leading role?

14 *Flame,* made in 1974, was the debut for which Paisley-born actor?

15 The Royal Scots Dragoon Guards reached number one in 1972 with which song?

ANSWERS

1. '9 to 5'. 2. Number 3 3. Boston 4. Anthony Asquith 5. *Separate Tables* 6. *The Untouchables* 7. David McCallum 8. Bill Forsyth 9. Gordon Jackson 10. 1994 11. The Communards 12. 'Goodnight Girl' 13. *The Longest Day* 14. Tom Conti 15. 'Amazing Grace'

SPORT

1 Which Fife town claims to have invented curling?

2 By what score did Stephen Hendry beat Jimmy White in the final of the 1993 Embassy World Snooker Championship?

3 Which Celtic player of the 20s and 30s once scored 8 goals in a single game against Dunfermline, and is the only British league player to have averaged a goal a game during his career?

4 Which Scot was captain of Kent Cricket Club from 1972 to 1976?

5 Which sporting club sported the first badge worn on the jacket?

6 Which forward played 28 times for Scotland and 492 league games for Liverpool in the post-war period?

7 Which club is Alan Rough most associated with?

8 Which was the first skating club in Britain?

9 Which Scottish club did Ian St John play for?

10 Where is the home of the Hon Society for Edinburgh Boaters?

11 Whom did Stephen Hendry defeat in the 1999 World Snooker Championship final?

12 Whose rules did the society of St Andrews Golfers adopt upon foundation in 1754?

13 Which Edinburgh golfing club predates the Hon. Company of Edinburgh Golfers?

14 Which famous cricket club did Scotsman Richard Nairn found?

15 Which Scottish cyclist won the 4000 m Individual Pursuit World Title in 1993?

ANSWERS

1. Limekilns 2. 18-5 3. Jimmy McCrory 4. Mike Denness 5. Duddinston Curling Club, in 1802 6. Billy Liddell 7. Partick Thistle 8. Edinburgh Skating Society (1778) 9. Motherwell 10. Union Canal 11. Mark Williams 12. Hon. Company of Edinburgh Golfers 13. Edinburgh Golfing Society, founded in 1735 14. Hambledon CC 15. Graeme Obree

PEOPLE

1   What nickname did Donald Caskie acquire during the Second World War?

2   How did he acquire it?

3   Which naval surgeon insisted that the British Admiralty supplied sailors with citrus fruits to cure scurvy?

4   Which Edinburgh anatomist received his specimens from the notorious grave robbers Burke and Hare?

5   Who was the mother of James VI?

6   Which Glasgow-born lieutenant-governor of Virginia recognised George Washington's talents and sent him to resist the French?

7   What nickname did this earn him?

8   Which suffragette and surgeon set up hospitals for troops in Serbia and Russia during the First World War?

9   Who is recognised as the father of social history?

10   How is Sir John Sholto Douglas better known?

11   With which sport is he associated?

12   Who was the first lecturer in Geography at the University of Edniburgh?

13   Of which famous geographical title was he the author, in 1895?

14   Which Scottish saint was known as the Apostle of Cumbria?

15   Where is he buried?

ANSWERS

1. The Tartan Pimpernell 2. By helping British servicemen escape to freedom 3. Dr James Lind 4. Dr Robert Knox 5. Mary, Queen of Scots 6. Robert Dinwiddie 7. 'Grandfather of the United States' 8. Elsie Inglis 9. David Hume 10. The 8th Marquis of Queensberry 11. Boxing: the Queensberry Rules 12. George Goudie Chisholm 13. Longmans Gazetteer of the World 14. Saint Mungo (or Kentigern) 15. Glasgow Cathedral

1   Who wrote *Thoughts on the Proposed Change of Currency* in 1826?

2   The renegade James More appears in which novel?

3   How did James Boswell's son Alexander die in 1822?

4   Samuel Pepys recorded the Dutch bombardment of which Scottish port in 1667?

5   Who revived Lindsay's *Ane Satire of the Thrie Estaits* for the first Ediuburgh Festival in 1947?

6   In which century did Thomas the Rhymer live?

7   Which seventh-century work celebrates the life of Saint Ninian?

8   Who wrote *Humphry Clinker*?

9   Which off-duty cleric is portrayed skating in a famous portait by Sir Henry Raeburn?

10 Souter Johnnie was immortalised in which Burns ballad?

11 Catherine Glover was the heroine of which Scott novel?

12 Ebeneezer Balfour is a character in which adventure novel?

13 Which 19th-century composer wrote the comic opera 'She Stops to Conquer'?

14 Who wrote 'Lord Ullin's Daughter'?

15 In which Scott novel would you encounter Douce Davie Deans?

ANSWERS

GENERAL KNOWLEDGE

1 Where is the nuclear power station situated on the northermost coast of mainland Scotland?

2 On which firth does Dundee stand?

3 Where is the administrative centre of the Highlands Council?

4 What is the greatest depth of Loch Ness?

5 Where is Blair Castle?

6 Who invaded 'Albion' in AD 80?

7 Which king instituted laws and early schools in 12th-century Scotland?

8 Who became known as the 'Guardian of Scotland' in 1297?

9 Which river runs between Ben Vrottan and Sguir Mor in Aberdeenshire?

10 From which oil field was the first offshore oil pumped in 1975?

11 How old was Donald Dewar when he became Scotland's First Minister in 1999?

12 In which county is the Cullerlie Stone Circle?

13 How is Deskford, Banffshire, pronounced locally?

14 John Farquhar Munro is an MSP for which party?

15 In which year did the Pictish king reject the Celtic church in favour of the Roman?

ANSWERS

1. Dounreay 2. Tay 3. Inverness 4. 754 feet 5. Pitlochry 6. Julius Agricola 7. David I 8. William Wallace 9. the Dee 10. North Sea Forties 11. 61 12. Aberdeenshire 13. 'Deskert' 14. Liberal Deomcrats 15. 685

1 Goat Fell is the highest point on which island?

2 Which mainland port is linked by ferry to Stornaway?

3 Findhorn lies at the mouth of which firth?

4 Which mountain lies just east of Bridge of Orchy?

5 Which loch extends west from the lower end of Loch Ness by Gairlochy?

6 What is the English for Beinn-na Faoghla?

7 What is the 'O of Arbroath'?

8 What term is given to the series of sharp turns on the highest point of the Glen Shee to Braemar road?

9 Which island lies across the Sound of Eigg from Eigg?

10 What sort of abbey was Dundrennan?

11 What was the name of the poltergeist that terrorised the Gilbert Campbell family in Wigtownshire?

12 The Clockmaben Stone stands on the shore of which firth?

13 Dobb's Linn, near Grey Mare's Tail, was a famous refuge for whom?

14 What was 'Locus Maponi'?

15 The early Christian centre of Whithorn is near which Wigtownshire town?

ANSWERS

1. Arran 2. Ullapool 3. Moray 4. Ben Dorain 5. Loch Arkaig 6. Benbecula 7. The Rose Window of the Abbey 8. Devil's Elbow 9. Muck 10. Cistercian 11. The Devil of Glenluce 12. Solway 13. Covenanters 14. An authorised tribal meeting place 15. Kirkmadrine

HISTORY

1 Whom did William Wallace kill in 1297, an action which triggered the revolt under his command?

2 What was Wallace's first important victory over the English, in the same year?

3 After which battle the following year was Wallace forced to resign the Guardianship of Scotland?

4 In which year was the Edinburgh Festival inaugurated?

5 Which battleship was sunk by a German U-boat in Scapa flow in 1939?

6 In the same year, where did the first German air raid on British vessels take place?

7 Which ship became the largest liner flying the British flag, in 1967?

8 The *Queen Mary* belonged to which shipping company?

9 How many people died in the 1971 Ibrox disaster?

10 Which castle was built on Loch Fyne in 1325?

11 In which year did the Tay Road Bridge open?

12 What was Edward Balliol's relationship with John Balliol?

13 In which battle was Edward Balliol defeated by the Scots?

14 In which year did this battle take place?

15 On which saint's day in 1557 and 1558 did Protestant mobs attack Catholic processions in Edinburgh?

ANSWERS

1. The Sheriff of Lanark, Hazelrig 2. Stirling 3. Falkirk (I) 4. 1947 5. *Royal Oak* 6. The Firth of Forth 7. *QE2* 8. White Star 9. 66 10. Tarbert 11. 1966 12. He was his son 13. Dupplin Moor 14. 1332 15. St Giles

1 Which Scottish trader was awarded Japan's 'Order of the Rising Sun' for his contributions towards modernising Japan?

2 Where did the Greenock-born pirate, Captain William Kidd, finally surrender to the authorities?

3 Who designed the (new) Royal Infirmary in Edinburgh?

4 What does 'Macadamisation' involve?

5 What was the middle name of the 'poet' William McGonagall?

6 What are 'Napier's Bones'?

7 What mathematical development did these lead to?

8 Who developed 'Napier's Bones'?

9 What does the 17th-century Skene Manuscript contain?

10 Which famous engineer was born in Phantasie, East Lothian?

11 Which poet founded the first travelling library in the UK?

12 Which Argyllshire parish gave its name to a chemical element, which was first found there?

13 Which Scottish builder constructed Wembley Stadium?

14 Which poet was a founder of the Scottish National Party?

15 What is the more common name for the St Andrews Psalter?

ANSWERS

1. Thomas Blake Glover 2. Boston 3. David Bryce 4. Covering a road surface with small broken stones to form a hard surface 5. Topaz 6. A type of multiplication table 7. Logarithms 8. John Napier 9. A collection of lute airs and dance music 10. John Rennie 11. Allan Ramsay 12. Strontium, discovered in Strontian parish 13. Sir Robert McAlpine 14. Hugh MacDiarmid 15. Wood's Psalter

TV & ENTERTAINMENT

1 Deborah Kerr starred opposite Robert Mitchum in which 1960 film about the Australian Outback?

2 Who took 'I Owe You Nothing' to number one in 1988?

3 Which actor shared a house with Errol Flynn in 1930s Hollywood?

4 Constant parties at this house gave it what nickname?

5 Who had a hit with 'Ma, He's Making Eyes At Me' in 1974?

6 What was the name of the 1974 sci-fi film which starred Sean Connery and was directed by John Boorman?

7 What links Jim Diamond with the Lone Ranger?

8 Which Hamilton-born actor starred in the 1979 film *The Human Factor?*

9 Who directed the 1972 film *Islands in the West?*

10 Who had a hit with 'Sweet Illusion' in 1973?

11 What links the TV series 'Upstairs Downstairs' with 'The Professionals'?

12 In which year did Sir Harry Lauder die?

13 Which American civil engineering project was the title of a Lonnie Donegan hit in the 1950s?

14 Which nationality is James Doohan, who plays 'Scotty' in 'Star Trek'?

15 Which appropriately named group had a hit with 'So Good To Be Back Home Again'?

ANSWERS

1. *The Sundowners* 2. Bros 3. David Niven 4. Cirrhosis-by-the-Sea 5. Lena Zavaroni 6. *Zardoz* 7. 'Hi ho silver', a Diamond hit and a Lone Ranger's catchphrase 8. Nicol Williamson 9. Bill Forsyth 10. Junior Campbell 11. Both starred Gordon Jackson 12. 1950 13. Grand Coolie Dam 14. Canadian 15. The Tourists

1   In which year did the Society of St Andrews Golfers successfully petition the king to add the word 'Royal' to their title?

2   Where was the first municipal bowling green?

3   In which year was it founded?

4   Which Hibs and Dundee player was nicknamed 'Scotland's Stanley Matthews'?

5   Which Spurs and Scotland player was killed by lightning on the golf course in 1964 at the age of 26?

6   Which Scot captained England in cricket in the 1970s?

7   How many times did he play for England?

8   When was golf first mentioned in a Scottish document?

9   How was it mentioned?

10 Who was the Celtic and Scotland goalkeeper who died as a result of a collision in a Rangers-Celtic match in 1931?

11 Who was the last home-based Scot to win the Open Championship in golf?

12 In what year did he win?

13 In which year did Parliament pass a law prohibiting football?

14 What was Scotland's FIFA ranking in 1997?

15 In which year did Stephen Hendry beat Jimmy White 18-17 at the Embassy World Snooker Championship after White missed an easy black in the final frame?

ANSWERS

1. 1834 2. Edinburgh 3 1860 . 4. Gordon Smith 5. John White 6. Mike Denness 7. 28
8. 1457 9. A prohibitive decree 10. John Thomson 11. Willie Auchterlonie 12. 1883
13. 1457 14. 37 15. 1994

PEOPLE

1. What title did Sir Ralph Alexander Cochrane hold during the Second World War?

2. In which year was Charles Rennie Mackintosh born?

3. In which year did the novelist Neil Munro die?

4. In which year was Mary, Queen of Scots forced to abdicate?

5. Who discovered that quinine bark acted as a cure for malaria?

6. With which invention is Andrew Meikle associated?

7. What was Keir Hardie's job before entering politics?

8. On which island was the great explorer of Canada, Sir Alexander Mackenzie, born?

9. How old was Saint Mungo when he died?

10. Which famous novelist and journalist was born at Inverary in 1860?

11. In what year did Sir Dugald Clerk invent the two-stroke Clerk Cycle Gas Engine?

12. Who made the song 'A Wee Doch an Doras' popular?

13. Where was Sir Alec Douglas Home born?

14. In which year did he become Prime Minister?

15. What did he have to do first?

ANSWERS

1. Air Chief Marshall of the RAF 2. 1868 3. 1930 4. 1567 5. George Cleghorn 6. Threshing machine 7. Miner 8. Lewis 9. Ninety-five 10. Neil Munro 11. 1877 12. Sir Harry Lauder 13. London 14. 1963 15. Renounce his title (the Earldom of Home)

1 In which Scott novel would you encounter the butler Caleb Balderstone?

2 In which unfinished novel would you meet Adam Weir?

3 Who dramatised Kenneth Grahame's *Wind in the Willows*?

4 What was the title of the dramatised version?

5 Who wrote the novel *The Silver Darlings*?

6 With which comic hero is the novelist Hugh Foulis associated?

7 Hugh Foulis is a pen-name for which novelist?

8 Who wrote the folk song 'The Laird o' Cockpen'?

9 What title is often bestowed on John Barbour (1320-1395)?

10 In which decade did he write *The Bruce*?

11 At which point in the hero's life does Barbour's story end?

12 Which 17th-century native of Cromarty was a translator of Rabelais?

13 Which mathematical treatise did he also publish, in 1645?

14 *Blanket of the Dark* is a novel by which author?

15 What profession did the writer Allan Ramsay pursue before turning to literature?

ANSWERS

1. *Bride of Lammermoor* 2. *Weir of Hermiston* 3. A A Milne 4. *Toad of Toad Hall* 5. Neil Gunn 6. Para Handy 7. Neil Munro 8. Lady Nairne 9. 'The Father of Scottish Literature' 10. 1370s 11. Victory at Bannockburn 12. Sir Thomas Urquhart 13. 'Trissotetras' 14. John Buchan 15. Wigmaking

GENERAL KNOWLEDGE

1   In which year did Edward I issue the Ordinance for theGovernment of Scotland?

2   In whch year did the first Scottish Parliament meet?

3   Complete the following famous rhyme: 'Ae mile o' wortha worth o' Dee...'

4   In which county is the village Fettersso?

5   The conical grassy hill of Dunnideer looms above which Aberdeesnshore village?

6   Following the 1975 government reforms, in which two regions does Loch Indorb lie?

7   Which city was burned by the Hebridean Alexander in 1429?

8   What was Alexander's title?

9   Who strode across the floor of the Scottish Parliament to shake Donald Dewar's hand to 'show I bear him no malice'?

10   Which was Robert the Bruce's first important victory over the English?

11   In which year did this battle take place?

12   Who led 15,000 English soliders to defeat at the Battle of Pinkie?

13   In which year did this battle take place?

14   Who founded Gordonstoun School in 1934?

15   Who discovered the element helium?

ANSWERS

1. 1305 2. 1326 3. 'Except for salmon, stone and tree' 4. Kincardineshire 5. Insch 6. Grampian and Highland 7. Inverness 8. Lord of the Isles 9. Dennis Canavan 10. Louden Hill 11. 1307 12. the Duke of Somerset 13. 1547 14. Kurt Hahn 15. Sir William Ramsay

214

1 Johnnie Turner's Monument stands above which reservoir?

2 Ballater lies along which river?

3 Sweetheart Abbey towers above which town?

4 Craigcaffie Castle, Stranraer, was a stronghold of which family?

5 For how many miles before its mouth does the River Tweed lie in England?

6 In which year did East Lothian cease to exist as a county?

7 Where were six favourites of James III hanged in 1483?

8 The toll-house at Lamberton served as what from 1798 to 1858?

9 In which town could you witness the 'Cleikum ceremony'?

10 In which Berwickshire town did Thomas the Rhymer spend his life?

11 Where is the Netherbow Arts Centre?

12 Thanes Castle is also known by which name?

13 Where could you attend the 'Braw Lads Gathering'?

14 Which was the last pre-Reformation abbey to be built in Scotland?

15 Near which town would you find the Standing Stones of Torhousekie?

ANSWERS

1. Glenkiln 2. Dee 3. New Abbey 4. Neilsons 5. Two 6. 1975 7. Lauder Bridge 8. A marriage-house, as at Gretna Green 9. Innerleithen 10. Earlston 11. Edinburgh 12. Tinnis Castle 13. Galashiels 14. Sweetheart Abbey 15. Wigtown

215

HISTORY

1 By which treaty were the Western Isles annexed by the Scottish Crown?

2 In which year did the Forth Road Bridge open?

3 Who selected John Balliol as King of Scotland?

4 In which year was Balliol so selected?

5 In which country did racing driver Jim Clark die in 1968?

6 In which year did British Steel close the Ravenscraig works?

7 Which king conquered Argyll in 1222?

8 In which year was North Sea oil first piped ashore?

9 In which year did Pope John Paul II visit Scotland?

10 Which king died at Kerrera?

11 In which year did the oil tanker *Braer* run aground?

12 In which Shetland bay did it founder?

13 In which year was the Stone of Destiny finally returned to Scotland?

14 Which king was married to 'the Saintly Queen'?

15 The sinking of which ship in the Sound of Eriskay in 1941 inspired the film *Whisky Galore*?

ANSWERS

1. Treaty of Perth 2. 1964 3. Edward I of England 4. 1292 5. West Germany 6. 1992 7. Alexander II 8. 1975 9. 1982 10. Alexander II 11. 1993 12. Quendale Bay 13. 1996 14. Malcolm III 15. SS *Politician*

TRIVIA

1 What is the official name of the Poppy Appeal?

2 For how many years did Scotland and England remain separate after the accession of James VI as James I of England?

3 Which Scot became the first Prime Minister of Canada?

4 Under whom did the artist Allan Ramsay study in London?

5 What connects East Lothian and Lake Havasu, Arizona?

6 Which famous Scottish Lord was an MP for Southampton in the 1940s?

7 Who left a large collection of anatomical specimens, coins and minerals to the Glasgow Museum, which then took its name from his?

8 Who founded the first travelling library in the UK?

9 Why was biblical scholar William Robertson-Smith dismissed from his job at Aberdeen University?

10 How did this dismissal arise?

11 What role did Flora Macdonald play in the American War of Independence?

12 Which dunce is now venerable?

13 In which year did the Vatican elevate him to 'Venerable' status?

14 Who discovered the element helium?

15 Which invention, often ascribed to Sir Isaac Newton, was developed three years earlier in Scotland?

ANSWERS

1. The Earl Haig Fund 2. 104 3. Sir John Alexander MacDonald 4. William Hogarth 5. The birthplace of John Rennie and the final destination for the London Bridge he designed 6. Lord Keith 7. William Hunter 8. Allan Ramsay 9. For heresy 10. He questioned the validity of parts of the Old Testament 11. Recruiting Scots to fight for the British in North Carolina 12. John Duns Scotus 13. 1991 14. Sir William Ramsay 15. The reflecting telescope (invented by James Gregory)

1 Sir Harry Lauder took the title from which of his hits as the title of his 1928 autobiography?

2 Which film director was spent much of the Second World War in Rome as part of the Psychological Warfare Branch?

3 Who had a hit with 'Hazell' in 1978?

4 What links Lonnie Donegan with Richard Wagner?

5 What was the name of the only chart hit by Love and Money, from 1986?

6 Who starred in *The First of the Few* and *The Way Ahead* between active service in the Second World War?

7 What was the only chart hit for Mad Jocks, in 1987?

8 Who directed the 1994 film *Being Human*?

9 Who sang about Cousin Norman in 1971?

10 In which film did Sean Connery first play James Bond?

11 In which year was that film released?

12 Who took the phonetically spelt 'Kayleigh' to number two in 1985?

13 Who sang about 'The Man Who Sold the World' in 1974?

14 Which guitarist had a hit with 'Going Home' in 1983?

15 Sydney Devine had only one chart hit, in 1978. What was its title?

ANSWERS

1. 'Roamin' in the Gloamin' 2. Alexander Mackendrick 3. Maggie Bell 4. Lorelei 5. 'Candybar Express' 6. David Niven 7. 'Jock Mix' 8. Bill Forsyth 9. Marmalade 10. *Dr No* 11. 1962 12. Marillion 13. Lulu 14. Mark Knopfler 15. 'Scotland Forever'

SPORT

1 Which is the only manufacturer of golf balls in Scotland?

2 Who is the most-capped Scottish goalkeeper ever?

3 Which Scot introduced the middle stump in cricket?

4 Who was Scotland's manager for the 1978 World Cup?

5 Who was WPGA champion in 1998?

6 Which is the most northerly team in the Scottish Football League?

7 Of which player did Don Revie say 'When he plays on snow, he doesn't leave any footprints'?

8 Which course has the longest championship hole in Britain?

9 Which hole is it?

10 How long is the hole?

11 Who was the first king to play golf?

12 Who said 'The ideal board of directors should be made up of three men - two dead and the other dying'?

13 What was Colin Montgomerie's record amount won in a single year on the European tour?

14 In which year did he achieve this?

15 How many holes long was the Old Course at St Andrews when it was first played?

ANSWERS

1. Sonido 2. Jim Leighton 3. Richard Nairn 4. Ally Macleod 5. Catriona Matthew 6. Ross County 7. Eddie Gray 8. Troon 9. Sixth 10. 577 yards 11. James IV 12. Tommy Docherty 13. £875,146 14. 1996 15. 22

PEOPLE

1 Which two-time Oscar winner, born in Aberfeldy, had Hollywood roles in *Birth of a Nation*, *National Velvet* and *Intolerance*?

2 What was the longest run of Grand Prix victories achieved by Jim Clark?

3 With what type of painting was William McTaggart associated?

4 What links Kincardine, Fife, with hot cups of tea?

5 Which actor, born in Kirriemuir in 1909, was nevertheless considered by Hollywood to be the 'quintessential Englishman'?

6 James Pillans invented what in the early 19th-century to teach geography?

7 Where was Margaret, Malcolm III's Queen, born?

8 Matthew Forster Heddle wrote a seminal book on what aspect of Scotland in 1901?

9 In which year did Richard Noble become the fastest man on Earth?

10 Archibald Cronin, creator of Doctor Finlay, trained as what himself?

11 Saint Ninian lived along the shores of which firth?

12 Which famous explorer died trying to find the source of the River Niger in Africa?

13 Who published his *Theory of the Earth* in 1785?

14 What ingredient did Charles Mackintosh apply to rubber sheeting strengthened by cloth to create the fabric in the raincoats that bear his name?

15 Who wrote *Highland River*?

ANSWERS

1. Donald Crisp 2. Seven 3. Landscapes 4. It is the birthplace of Sir James Dewar, inventor of the vacuum flask 5. David Niven 6. The blackboard and coloured chalk 7. Hungary 8. Mineralogy 9. 1983, when he beat the land speed record 10. Also as a doctor 11. Solway 12. Mungo Park 13. James Hutton 14. Naptha 15. Neil Gunn

1 Which 19th-century composer wrote the oratorio 'Saint John the Baptist'?

2 The ghostwriter H Kingsley Long was involved in the publication of which hard-hitting Glasgow novel of the 1930s?

3 In which Scott novel would you encounter Meg Murdockson?

4 In which year was Muriel Spark's novel *The Prime of Miss Jean Brodie* published?

5 In which century did Blind Harry write?

6 Blind Harry's major work concerns which Scottish hero?

7 Which author traced his lineage back to Adam in a 1652 book?

8 What was the name of this book?

9 Which early 18th century writer tried to open a theatre in Edinburgh although theatres were banned in the city?

10 Alexander Trocchi was associated with which Movement, usually associated with the United States?

11 Which author is credited with having published the word 'f**k' in print for the first time?

12 In which year was it printed?

13 Who wrote *The Corn King and the Snow Queen*, published in 1931?

14 Who wrote the folk song 'Will Ye No' Come Back Again'?

15 Who wrote the novel *Gap in the Curtain*?

ANSWERS

1. George Macfarren 2. *No Mean City* 3. *Heart of Midlothian* 4. 1961 5. 15th century 6. Robert the Bruce 7. Sir Thomas Urquhart 8. *Pantochronochanon* 9. Allan Ramsay 10. The Beat Movement 11. William Dunbar 12. 1508 13. Naomi Mitchison 14. Lady Nairne 15. John Buchan

GENERAL KNOWLEDGE

1 Bishop Turnbull is linked with the foundation of what in 1451?

2 What event of 1559 is seen as the real start of the Reformation in Scotland?

3 Who led the English at the Battle of Bannockburn?

4 In which county is the Tower of Drum?

5 How many seats did the Liberal Democrats win in the Scottish parliamentary elections of May 1999?

6 Kildrummy Castle, Aberdeenshire, was created by which Scottish saint in the 13th century?

7 Which French king took refuge in Scotland in the 19th-century after being expelled from his throne?

8 Which treaty of 1328 officially recognized Scotland's independence?

9 Which two kings signed this treaty?

10 Of which Kincardineshire village has it been said that 'the only regular feature about it is its irregularity'?

11 Who was captured by the English in 1406?

12 North Sea Oil was pumped initially to which refinery in November 1975?

13 In which year did the Black Death arrive in Scotland?

14 In which year did Mary, Queen of Scots return to Scotland from France?

15 At which battle did Robert the Bruce defeat Comyn of Buchan?

ANSWERS

1. University of Glasgow 2. John Knox's sermon in Perth 3. Edwar II 4. Aberdeenshire 5. 17 6. St Gilbert 7. Charles X 8. Treaty of Northampton 9. Robert I and Edward III of England 10. Drumlithie 11. James I 12. Grangemouth 13. 1349 14. 1561 15. Inverurie

1 Where is the Strathclyde Arts Centre?

2 Which famous religious dissenter was born in Moniave?

3 Whom does Murray's Monument, near Newton Stewart, commemorate?

4 Where is the 60-foot Waterloo Tower, dedicated to 'our gallant Prussian allies'?

5 What was mined at Woodhead between 1830 and 1870?

6 Which castle belonged, in succession, to the Frasers, the Hays of Yester and the Dukes of Queensberry?

7 George Square, Edinburgh, is dedicated to whom?

8 Gladsmuir claims which 'jingling Geordie' as a native?

9 Thirlestane Castle was built by which earls?

10 Galashiels lies on two sides of which body of water?

11 According to tradition, which three peaks were once united and were only split by Michael Scott, the Border Wizard?

12 Lothian saw the extinction of which species in 1700?

13 Where is Ramshorn Theatre?

14 Which clan for centuries had a seat at Mochram?

15 Where is the Scotch Whisky Heritage Centre?

ANSWERS

1. Glasgow 2. James Renwick, Covenanter martyr 3. Dr Alexander Murray, a gifted 19th-century linguist 4. New Abbey 5. Lead 6. Neidpath 7. The architect George Brown 8. George Heriot 9. Lauderdale 10. Gala Water 11. Eildon Hills 12. Wolf 13. Glasgow 14. Dunbar 15. Edinburgh

HISTORY

1 Where did the Romans defeat the Picts in Scotland's first recorded battle in 84 AD?

2 A split in which clan resulted in the division between Lewis and Harris?

3 At the bottom of which town's harbour is there supposedly a treasure-laden Spanish galleon, sunk in mysterious circumstances in 1588?

4 Which king built Edinburgh Castle?

5 In which century was the University of St Andrews founded?

6 Which king founded the abbeys of Scone and Inchcoln?

7 From what illness did Robert the Bruce die?

8 Near which city was the Battle of Bannockburn fought in 1314?

9 Which battle was fought on 17 July 1689 in Perthshire?

10 Where was Malcom II murdered?

11 Who took the Stone of Destiny to England?

12 Which decisive Scottish victory over the Norwegians obtained the Hebrides from Norway?

13 Which Norwegian king's fleet was defeated in this battle?

14 Which city received its charter from William the Lion in 1180?

15 In which year did Sir Alexander Fleming discover penicillin?

ANSWERS

1. Mons Graupius 2. MacLeod 3. Tobermory 4. Malcolm III (Malcolm Canmore) 5. 15th (1411) 6. Alexander I 7. Leprosy 8. Stirling 9. Battle of Killiecrankie 10. Glamis Castle 11. Edward I 12. Battle of Largs 13. King Haaken 14. Inverness 15. 1928

1 Who propounded the theory of Uniformitarianism?

2 What did this theory seek to explain?

3 Who set up the Indian Institute for Science in Bangalore?

4 Where is the engineer John Rennie buried?

5 Which Cabinet position did Manny Shinwell hold in 1946?

6 Which Cabinet position did Manny Shinwell hold in 1947-51?

7 Who named twin volcanoes after his ships *Erebus* and *Terror*?

8 By which name was the Dundee-born missionary Mary Slessor known to the Nigerians?

9 What was the nickname of the subtle 16th-century negotiator William Maitland?

10 Of which Italian's name is this a transliteration?

11 Who were the 'Gentlemen of Mearns'?

12 Who published the first edition of *Encyclopaedia Britannica*?

13 In what year was it published?

14 The invention of the iron plough is credited to which 18th-century Scot?

15 Who discovered the element argon?

ANSWERS

1. James Hutton 2. The geological history of the Earth 3. Sir William Ramsay 4. St Paul's Cathedral, London 5. Minister of Fuel and Power 6. Secretary of State for Defence 7. Sir James Clark Ross 8. 'Great Mother' 9. Michael Wylie 10. Machiavelli 11. Protestant Lords of Kincardineshire 12. William Smellie 13. 1768 14. James Small 15. Sir William Ramsay

TV & ENTERTAINMENT

1 In which year did the Tourists have a number four hit with 'I Only Want To Be With You'?

2 Which 1976 song was the highest-placed song by Paul Jones?

3 Which Scottish-born actor starred in *The Moon is Blue*?

4 The Royal Scots Dragoon Guards had a hit with which Christmas song in 1972?

5 Who decided that 'Thinkin' ain't for me' in 1967?

6 Who directed *The Man in the White Suit*?

7 What was the first chart hit for Texas, in 1989?

8 What was the first chart hit for Wet Wet Wet, in 1987?

9 Which two other songs, from the same year, climbed one place higher to number five?

10 In which 1971 film does Sean Connery mastermind a complicated heist in an American apartment building?

11 Who sang about the 'Gamblin' bar room blues' in 1975?

12 What was the title of the Scottish World Cup Squad's single, released in the previous year?

13 Who sang the 1994 number one hit 'Inside'?

14 Who directed the 1977 film *The Legend of Los Tayos*?

15 Who sang about a 'Lazy Lover' in 1996?

ANSWERS

1. 1979 2. 'High Time' 3. David Niven 4. 'Little Drummer Boy' 5. Paul Jones 6. Alexander Mackendrick 7. 'I Don't Want a Lover' 8. 'Wishing I Was Lucky' 9. 'Sweet Little Mystery' and 'Angel Eyes' 10. *The Anderson Tapes* 11. Sensational Alex Harvey Band 12. 'Easy Easy' 13. Stiltskin 14. Bill Forsyth 15. Supernaturals

SPORT

1 Who were Scotland's second opponents in the 1998 World Cup Finals in France?

2 Where would you find the Swilcan Burn?

3 Who was Scotland's manager for the 1990 World Cup Finals in Spain?

4 Where was the first professional golf tournament held?

5 In what year did it take place?

6 Who won the tournament?

7 Who holds the Scottish record for batting in cricket?

8 What did he score and in how much time?

9 For which team was he playing?

10 Who won the European Cup-Winners' Cup in 1972?

11 Who won the European Cup-Winners' Cup in 1983?

12 What is Craigentinny?

13 Which was the first lacrosse club in Britain?

14 When was it founded?

15 Whom did Stephen Hendry beat 18-9 at the 1995 Embassy World Snooker Championship?

ANSWERS

1. Norway 2. the Old Course at St Andrews 3. Andy Roxburgh 4. Prestwick 5. 1860 6. Willie Park 7. Archibald Campbell Maclaren 8. 424 in 7 hours, 50 minutes 9. Lancashire (against Somerset in Taunton) 10. Rangers 11. Aberdeen 12. A golf course in Edinburgh 13. Glasgow Lacrosse Club 14. 1867 15. Nigel Bond

PEOPLE

1   Who introduced the cypress *Cupressus Lawsonii* to Britain?

2   What was the name of the colony that Robert Dale Owen founded in Indiana in 1825?

3   To where in North America did Flora Macdonald emigrate?

4   James Paterson (1770-1840), a Musselburgh native, developed the process that is still to used today to make what by machine?

5   Why did Allan Pinkerton leave Glasgow hurriedly in 1842?

6   Which Scottish geologist led a survey of the Russian Empire between 1840 and 1845?

7   Where was the engineer John Rennie born?

8   Where is he buried?

9   Which scientist, chiefly noted for his discovery of the noble gases, also did pioneering work in radioactivity?

10 What role did James Robertson Justice make famous in a series of 'Doctor' films?

11 Who was Edinburgh's first Medical Officer of Health?

12 With which ill-fated project was William Paterson, the noted financier, associated?

13 Which city benefitted from a large bequest from Sir Thomas Lipton upon his death in 1931?

14 Which entrepreneur was known as 'Concrete Bob'?

15 Which Scottish pirate was rewarded by New York City in 1691?

ANSWERS

1. Charles Lawson 2. New Harmony 3. North Carolina 4. Fishing nets 5. Because of his involvement in left-wing protests 6. Sir Roderick Impey Murchison 7. Phantassie, East Lothian 8. St Paul's, London 9. Sir William Ramsay 10. Sir Lancelot Spratt 11. Sir Henry Duncan Littlejohn 12. The Darien Farce 13. Glasgow 14. Sir Robert McAlpine 15. William Kidd (Captain Kidd)

MUSIC & LITERATURE

1   Who made a famous translation of Virgil's *Aeniad* into Scots?

2   Who founded Britain's first lending library?

3   Where and when was it founded?

4   In which year did the philosopher David Hume die?

5   Which famous writer on economic matters published his most famous work in the same year?

6   Who wrote the novel *The Man of Feeling*?

7   Who wrote the novel *Lanark,* now recognised as one of the great novels of the century?

8   In which Scott novel would you encounter Henry Morton of Milnwood?

9   Who wrote the words to 'Rule Britannia'?

10   Who wrote the 1981 book *Lanark*?

11   In which Scott novel would you meet Madge Wildfire?

12   The character Frank Innes features in which unfininshed novel?

13   Who wrote *The Testament of Cresseid*?

14   By which Chaucer work was this book inspired?

15   Which 17th-century author claimed to be descended from a third century BC prince called Esormon of Achaia?

ANSWERS

1. Gavin Douglas 2. Allan Ramsay 3. High Street, Edinburgh 4. 1776 5. Adam Smith 6. Henry Mackenzie 7. Alasdair Gray 8. *Castle Dangerous* 9. James Thomson 10. Alasdair Gray 11. *Heart of Midlothian* 12. *Weir of Hermiston* 13. Robert Henryson 14. *Troilus and Criseyde* 15. Sir Thomas Urquhart

GENERAL KNOWLEDGE

1　In which year was Darnley, husband of Mary, Queen of Scots, murdered?

2　What product of Mrs Janet Keiller was first produced in a Dundee factory in 1797?

3　In which year was Celtic Football Club founded?

4　The 'Trot of Turriff' was the first serious clash in which war?

5　What was printed for the first time in Scotland in 1579?

6　In which area of Caithness did a peat-burning electric station operate in the late 1950s?

7　In which year did John Knox die?

8　In which year were the Cameron Highlanders raised?

9　The MacIans of Ardnamurchan were a branch of which clan?

10　Which Cabinet post did Lord Reith hold from 1940 to 1942?

11　The MacLeods famously massacred the MacDonalds in a cave on which island?

12　In which year did the massacre take place?

13　In which year was Regent Moray killed by nobles?

14　Who discovered the element xenon?

15　Where is the Old Pretender buried?

ANSWERS

1. 1567 2. Marmalade 3. 1888 4. The Civil War 5. The Bible 6. Braehour 7. 1572 8. 1793 9. Clan Donald 10. Minister of Works 11. Eigg 12. 1594 13. 1570 14. Sir William Ramsay 15. St Peter's, Rome

PLACES

1 Where is the Museum of the Royal Highland Fusiliers?

2 In which city is the Museum of Childhood?

3 Which Aberdeenshire village has a March of the Clansmen each September?

4 Which Lowland town was renamed Newton Douglas briefly in the 1780s?

5 Where would you find the 'Hurzcars Rocks'?

6 A stretch of earthworks known as 'Picts' Work Ditch' lies above which town?

7 Near which Edinburgh landmark are Samson's Ribs?

8 In which Midlothian village is there a large sycamore known as 'Ben Jonson's Tree'?

9 Which famous financier was born in Torthorwald?

10 Which well-preserved medieval motte lies 2 miles north-west of Dalbeattie?

11 Where was the *Miracula Nynie* written in the seventh century?

12 Threave Castle was a stronghold of which clan?

13 Priorwood Gardens are adjacent to which abbey?

14 Which Dumfries and Galloway mining area was referred to as 'God's treasure-house in Scotland'?

15 In which city is the Tron Theatre?

ANSWERS

1. Glasgow 2. Edinburgh 3. Aboyne 4. Newton Stewart 5. Eyemouth 6. Galashiels 7. Arthur's Seat 8. Hawthornden 9. William Paterson, founder of the Bank of England 10. Motte of Urr 11. Whithorn 12. Douglas 13. Melrose 14. Wanlockhead 15. Glasgow

HISTORY

1   In which year did James VI succeed Mary, Queen of Scots?

2   How did Kirkpatrick Macmillan miss out on a fortune in the 19th century?

3   In which year did John Logie Baird demonstrate television?

4   In which year was Radar invented?

5   Who was the inventor?

6   How long did William the Lion reign?

7   Which treaty with the English, signed by William the Lion, plunged Scotland into debt?

8   After defeat in which battle was William forced to sign this treaty?

9   What was John Graham of Claverhouse, Viscount dundee, better known as?

10 In which year did the Church of Scotland unite with the United Free Church?

11 Scottish railways were absorbed into which two lines in 1921?

12 How many people were killed at the Ibrox Stadium collapse of 1902?

13 Which Glaswegian was central in bringing about the Confederation of Canada?

14 In which year did this Confederation take place?

15 Which pope canonised 'the saintly queen'?

ANSWERS

1. 1567 2. By failing to patent the pedal bicycle 3. 1926 4. 1935 5. Sir Robert Watson-Watt 6. 49 years 7. Falaise 8. Alnwick 9. 'Bonnie Dundee' 10. 1929 11. L.N.E.R. and L.M.S. 12. 20 13. Sir John MacDonald 14. 1867 15. Innocent IV

1 After whom is the Ross Ice Shelf named?

2 On which continent is this ice shelf?

3 Who founded the Boy's Brigade?

4 In which year did he found the brigade?

5 Arthur Anderson (1792-1868) was a benefactor in Lerwick, where there are buildings named after him. Of which maritime company was he the co-founder?

6 Which English architect designed Glasgow University?

7 Who rebuilt Holyrood House in the 1670s?

8 Who instituted Edinburgh's 'one o'clock gun'?

9 What official title did he hold?

10 At which university did Adam Smith teach?

11 Who built Waterloo Bridge, London?

12 Whose use of chloroform during childbirth brought wide acceptance to Sir James Young Simpson's medical development?

13 Who was the first archbishop of Glasgow?

14 In which county was David Livingstone born?

15 Who discovered the element neon?

ANSWERS

1. Sir James Clark Ross 2. Antarctica 3. Sir William Alexander Smith 4. 1883 5. Peninsular and Oriental Steam Navigation Company (P&O) 6. Sir George Gilbert Scott 7. Sir William Bruce 8. Charles Piazzi Smyth 9. Astronomer Royal for Scotland 10. Glasgow 11. John Rennie 12. Queen Victoria 13. Robert Blackadder 14. Lanarkshire 15. Sir William Ramsay

TV & ENTERTAINMENT

1 The film *Four Weddings and a Funeral* featured a smash single for which Scottish group?

2 What was the title of this song?

3 Who had an international hit with the same song more than 30 years before?

4 Who claimed to be a 'One Man Woman' in 1980?

5 Who wrote the novel *Housekeeping*, which Bill Forsyth filmed in 1987?

6 With which aggravatingly titled song did Middle of the Road reach number one in 1972?

7 What was the title of the Scottish World Cup Squad's 1982 single?

8 In which 1969 film does Sean Connery play a member of a secret Irish organisation in a Pennsylvania mining community?

9 Who had a hit with 'Julia says No' in 1995?

10 What were the titles of David Niven's two best-selling autobiographies?

11 Who had a hit with 'If I Was' in 1985?

12 Which of Alexander Mackendrick's films is a searing account of gossip columnists in New York City?

13 Who had a hit with 'Machinery' in 1982?

14 Who had a hit with 'Alive and Kicking' in 1985?

15 Who has played Alistair Balman in 'Taggart' and Dr John Finlay in two series of 'Doctor Finlay'?

ANSWERS

1. Wet Wet Wet 2. Love is All Around 3. the Troggs 4. Sheena Easton 5. Marilynne Robinson 6. 'Chirpy Chirpy Cheep Cheep' 7. 'We Have a Dream' 8. The Molly Maguires 9. Wet Wet Wet 10. *The Moon's a Balloon* and *Bring on the Empty Horses* 11. Midge Ure 12. *Sweet Smell of Success* 13. Sheena Easton 14. Simple Minds 15. David Rintoul

SPORT

1 What was the final score in the match between Scotland and Brazil in the 1998 World Cup Finals in France?

2 How many stones are thrown in curling to compete an end?

3 What was the title of Alan Hansen's autobiography?

4 Who partnered 1998 World Motor Racing Champion Mikka Hakkinen in the McLaren-Mercedes team?

5 Which bowler got the most stumpings in one innings in a game involving Scotland?

6 What was his total?

7 What was his county team?

8 What happened 29 times between Inverness Thistle and Falkirk in 1978-9?

9 In which competition did this take place?

10 Which team won the first three Scottish Cup finals?

11 Over which three years did these occur?

12 Who is the only Scot to have played in four World Cups?

13 Where was the first women's golf tournament held?

14 Whom did Stephen Hendry beat 18-6 at the 1996 Embassy World Snooker Championship, giving him a record-matching sixth victory in the tournament?

15 Whose six-victory records did Hendry match with that 1996 victory?

ANSWERS

1. 2-1 to Brazil 2. 16 3. *Tall, Dark and Hansen* 4. David Coulthard 5. Henry Yarnold 6. Six 7. Worcestershire 8. Their match was postponed 9. Scottish Cup 10. Queen's Park 11. 1874-6 12. Jim Leighton 13. Musselburgh 14. Peter Ebdon 15. Ray Reardon and Steve Davis

PEOPLE

1 How old was Sir Robert McAlpine when he left school?

2 Who was implicated in the 'Babington Conspiracy'?

3 Who was Malcolm II's famous grandson?

4 Which Scottish-born statesman became US ambassador to India in 1853?

5 Who was his famous grandfather?

6 Which Edinburgh anatomist discovered the lymphatic system and noted its purpose?

7 What title did Lord Reith have at the inception of the BBC?

8 In which year did he assume this title?

9 In which Glasgow district was Allan Pinkerton born?

10 Which 19th-century geologist wrote the classic text *The Old Red Sandstone* in 1841?

11 What trade did he - appropriately - pursue before becoming a geologist?

12 From what disease was Lord Darnley recovering when he was killed in the 16th-Century?

13 It is believed that William Paterson promoted Union with England strongly in order to recoup losses he and his son made where?

14 What links Saint Columba with Queen Margaret?

15 Hamish MacCunn is best known for which work?

ANSWERS

1. Ten 2. Mary, Queen of Scots 3. Macbeth 4. Robert Dale Owen 5. Millionaire philanthropist Davd Dale 6. Alexander Monro (Secundus) 7. General manager 8. 1922 9. The Gorbals 10. Hugh Miller 11. Stone mason 12. Smallpox 13. Darien 14. The abbey at Iona: he founded it and she re-founded it in the 11th century 15. 'Land of Mountains and the Flood'

MUSIC & LITERATURE

1 In which century did Alexander Scott write?

2 For what type of literature is he best remembered?

3 In which Scott novel would you meet Peter Peebles?

4 In which language is Allan Ramsay's most famous poetry?

5 Who wrote the poem sequence *The Seasons*?

6 Which piece of symphonic music did it inspire?

7 Who is regarded as the father of Scottish theatre?

8 What is his most famous play?

9 For which king's marriage did he write this play?

10 How long did the first performance last?

11 In which Scott novel would you encounter Bartoline Saddletree?

12 Who wrote the 1652 book *Ekskybalauron*?

13 Which real-life polymath was its hero?

14 What distinction does this book have?

15 Who wrote the folk song 'The Land o' the Leal'?

ANSWERS

1. 16th-century 2. love poetry 3. *Redgauntlet* 4. Scots 5. James Thomson 6. Haydn's 'Oratorio' 7. Sir David Lindsay 8. *Ane Satyre of the Thrie Estaits* 9. James V 10. Nine hours 11. *Heart of Midlothian* 12. Sir Thomas Urquhart 13. The Admirable Crichton 14. Many consider it the first Scottish novel 15. Lady Nairne

1 What is the official residence of the reigning British monarch in Scotland?

2 Which town or city was formerly known as Devana?

3 What is Arthur's seat?

4 In which month does the Edinburgh Military Tattoo take place?

5 Which British based bird of prey breeds only in Scotland?

6 Where is the largest marine engineering centre in Britain?

7 What is a finnan haddie?

8 What are the two highest courts in the Scottish judicial system?

9 What is the popular name given to the Royal Highland regiment who wear dark coloured tartan kilts?

10 What type of animal is a Scottish Fold?

11 Who owns Glamis Castle?

12 What is the decorative embellishment on the Stone of Destiny?

13 In which year was the University of Edinburgh founded?

14 The year 1929 saw the union of which two religious denominations?

15 Which Irish monk founded a monastery at Applecross in AD 671?

ANSWERS

1. Holyrood House 2. Aberdeen 3. An extinct volcano 4. August 5. Osprey 6. Clydebank 7. Smoked haddock or kipper 8. High Court of Justiciary and Court of Sessions 9. Black Watch 10. Cat 11. Elizabeth II 12. A cross 13. 1582 14. Church of Scotland and United Free Church 15. Maelrubha

PLACES

1   What sticky substance is associated with Palnackie?

2   Near which town are the striking remains of the Rink Fort?

3   In which town are the Border Games held?

4   Who built Gosford House in Longiddry, East Lothian?

5   What famous event took place in 1556 at Calder House, Midlothian?

6   Which West Lothian mine was known locally as 'the Dardanelles' because of its date of sinking?

7   What type of factory was built at Ardeer, Ayrshire, in 1843?

8   The Ardgarten peninsula lies on which loch?

9   Puck's Glen is in which forest park?

10   In which town was the notorious Kirkdandie Fair held?

11   Why was it notorious?

12   In which Lanarkshire town could you once buy the weekly magazine *Iseivin Draugas?*

13   Calgary, Argyll, gave its name to a major city in which Canadian province?

14   What was the name of the famous 18th-century religious festival that took place in Cambuslang?

15   In which town did James IV see a ghost warning him of doom in the Battle of Flodden?

ANSWERS

1. Treacle 2. Galashiels 3. Innerleithen 4. Robert Adam 5. John Knox celebrated the first Holy Communion according to the Presbyterian rite 6. Whitburn 7. Dynamite 8. Loch Long 9. Argyll 10. Barr 11. Because local smugglers roamed freely through the streets 12. Bellshill: it was a Lithuanian immigrant publication 13. Alberta 14. The Cambuslang Wark 15. Linlithgow

HISTORY

1 Somerled, a Scot-Viking Lord of the Isles, was the progenitor of which clan?

2 Somerled's rise coincided with the ascent to the throne of which Scottish king?

3 In which year did the 'Highland Host' descend upon south-west Scotland?

4 In which year was St Kilda evacuated?

5 Where did Charles I, in a hopeless position, negotiate a truce with the Scots in 1641?

6 In which year did the Forth Rail Bridge open?

7 Which province was annexed by the Crown in 1134?

8 In which year was James VII (James II of England) crowned?

9 In which year was the Grampian Hydro-Electric Power Scheme initiated?

10 Where was a German battle fleet scuppered in 1919?

11 In which year was Charles II proclaimed King?

12 Scotland and England played the first Rugby International: in which year?

13 In which year was Galloway subjected to the Scottish Crown?

14 Who led the Scots Covenanting Army that showed its force by marching on Newcastle in 1640?

15 Which Lewis-born explorer travelled the length of a Canadian river which now carries his name?

ANSWERS

1. Clan Donald 2. Malcolm IV 3. 1678 4. 1930 5. Ripon 6. 1890 7. Moray 8. 1685 9. 1928 10. Scapa Flow 11. 1649 12. 1871 13. 1160 14. David Leslie 15. Sir Alexander Mackenzie

1 Who published the Edinburgh edition of Robert Burns's poems in 1787?

2 Who designed the new town area of Edinburgh?

3 Who designed the Glasgow School of Art?

4 Which soldier and colonial administrator, born on the Isle of Ulva, became known as the 'father of Australia'?

5 What was the first name of the inventor of macadamized roads?

6 Which product was Gregor Fisher advertising in his Baldy Man in the Photo Booth ad?

7 What was Kirkpatrick Macmillan's occupation?

8 What does Del Amitri mean in Greek?

9 What was the surname of the two brothers in the Bay City Rollers?

10 Which famous poet and bookseller was born in Leadhills in 1681?

11 In which field did his son also become famous?

12 How old was Labour leader John Smith when he died?

13 Who was the ballet dancer and choreographer born in Dunfermline in 1929, who became artistic director of the Royal Ballet in 1970, and was knighted in 1983?

14 Who was the founder of Creation Records?

15 Who built Southwark Bridge, London?

ANSWERS

1. William Smellie 2. James Craig 3. Charles Rennie Mackintosh 4. Lachlan Macquarie 5. John 6. Hamlet cigars 7. Blacksmith 8. From the womb 9. Longmuir 10. Allan Ramsay 11. Painting 12. Fifty-six 13. Sir Kenneth Macmillan 14. Alan McGee 15. John Rennie

TV & ENTERTAINMENT

1   Who co-starred with Sean Connery in *The Man Who Would be King?*

2   What was the first chart hit for the Bay City Rollers?

3   What is the name of the band formed in 1984 at Oban High School with Karen Matheson on vocals, who play traditional and Gaelic music from the West Highlands of Scotland?

4   Who is the lead singer with Fairground Attraction?

5   Who is Garbage's Edinburgh-born lead singer?

6   On which label did the Cocteau Twins record until signing for Fontana in 1992?

7   What was the name of Shirley Manson's first band?

8   True or false – Lloyd Cole was born in Scotland?

9   Which band had Top 20 hits in 1984 with *I'm Falling* and *Young at Heart?*

10   Who directed the 1955 film *The Maggie?*

11   Who was 'Kool in the Kaftan' in 1980?

12   How high in the charts did the Bay City Rollers hit 'Shang-a-lang' reach in 1974?

13   How high in the charts did the Bay City Rollers hit 'Sommerlove Sensation' reach in the same year?

14   Who played Miss Jean Brodie in the film *The Prime of Miss Jean Brodie?*

15   How high in the charts did the Eurythmics hit 'Here Comes the Rain Again' reach in 1984?

ANSWERS

1. Michael Caine 2. 'Keep on Dancing' 3. Capercaillie 4. Eddi Reader 5. Shirley Manson 6. 4AD 7. 'Goodbye Mr Mackenzie 8. False - he was born in Buxton, Derbyshire 9. The Bluebells 10. Alexander Mackendrick 11. B A Robertson 12. Number 2 13. Number 3 14. Maggie Smith 15. Number 8

1 Who scored Scotland's first goal in the 1998 World Cup Finals in France?

2 Which is the highest British golf course?

3 How high above sea level is it (within 100 feet)?

4 What did Lt Philip Mitford of the Queen's Own Cameron Highlanders achieve in a Malta Governor's Cup cricket match in 1903?

5 What was the total?

6 Which teams contested the first football match to be televised live in Scotland?

7 In which year was it broadcast?

8 What is the highest score in a first class Scottish football match?

9 In which year did this match take place?

10 What is the lowest aggregate four-round score in an Open?

11 Who made this record score?

12 On which course and in which year was it made?

13 By what score did Hibs beat 42nd Highlanders in 1881?

14 In which year was the first women's golf tournament held?

15 Who were the competitors?

ANSWERS

1. John Collins 2. Leadhills 3. 1,500 feet 4. Most runs off a single ball 5. 11 runs 6. Aberdeen and Hearts 7. 1986 8. 36-0 in a Scottish Cup tie between Arbroath and Bon Accord 9. 1885 10. 268 11. Tom Watson 12. Turnberry (1977) 13. 22-1 14. 1811 15. Fishwives

PEOPLE

1 Canmore means 'big head': how did Malcolm III acquire the epithet?

2 Who foiled a plot to assassinate President Abraham Lincoln on his way to be inaugurated in 1861?

3 Which other famous Scottish painter did Allan Ramsay employ as an assistant?

4 Who founded the Edinburgh Royal Infirmary?

5 In which year did Bill Shankly die?

6 What is the full title of Adam Smith's pivotal book on economics?

7 Who was Queen Victoria's Sculptor in Scotland?

8 Where was Alistair Sim born?

9 Which mathematician and physicist contributed greatly to the study of electro-magnetism in the 19th century?

10 Which modern branch of physics owes much to this research?

11 What organisation did Sir William Alexander Smith form in 1883?

12 In which Olympic sport did Jackie Stewart excel after retiring from driving?

13 James Small (1730-93) was resonsible for which agricultural invention?

14 Who was the father of Mary, Queen of Scots?

15 Which founder of the Royal College of Physicians was also the Cartographer-Royal for Scotland?

ANSWERS

1. Because of his intelligence 2. Allan Pinkerton 3. Alexander Nasmyth 4. Alexander Monro Primus 5. 1981 6. *An Inquiry into the Nature and Causes of Wealth of Nations* 7. Sir John Steell 8. Edinburgh 9. James Clerk Maxwell 10. Quantum physics 11. The Boy's Brigade 12. Clay-pigeon shooting 13. The iron plough 14. James V 15. Sir Robert Sibbald

1 Which poem by Sir Walter Scott concerns Roland de Vaux?

2 How did the 17th-century author Sir Thomas Urquhart supposedly die in 1660?

3 To whom did Scott dedicate *Waverley?*

4 How did he described him in this dedication?

5 With what literary style was the work of Ian Maclaren associated?

6 Who wrote the 1995 play *A Meeting With the Monster?*

7 On whose life is this play based?

8 Who wrote the novel *The Book of Man?*

9 On whose life is this work loosely based?

10 Which crime novelist went on to great success with romantic fiction?

11 Under which pseudonym do these romantic works appear?

12 Robert Burns was born a year after the death of which poet, whose work in Scots opened the door for Burns's own work?

13 In which year did English-born director John McGrath found the 7:84 Theatre Company in Glasgow?

14 In which Scott novel would you encounter the Laird of Bucklaw?

15 For what type of writing is Dorothy Dunnett famous?

ANSWERS

1. *The Bridal of Triermain* 2. Of laughter, upon hearing of the Restoration of Charles II 3. Henry Mackenzie 4. 'Our Scottish Addison' 5. The Kailyard School 6. David Millar 7. Alexander Trocchi 8. Barry Graham 9. Alexander Trocchi 10. Hugh C Rae 11. Jessica Stirling 12. Allan Ramsay 13. 1971 14. *Bride of Lammermoor* 15. Historical novels

245

GENERAL KNOWLEDGE

1 In which year was the first colour photograph taken?

2 Which famous scientist oversaw this event?

3 What tragedy occurred at the Glen Cinema, Paisley, in 1929?

4 In which year was racing driver Jim Clark killed?

5 Who built the Inverness-shire township of Bernera?

6 Which famous headland was named 'hvarf' (turning point) by the Norse because of its dangerous reefs and cliffs?

7 Conon Bridge, designed by Telford, lies just over 2 miles south of which town?

8 In which county would you find the Cam Loch?

9 Lord Lovat bought which fort and lands for £5000 in 1867?

10 When was Winnie Ewing first elected as an MEP?

11 What is her European constitency?

12 In which county would you find Clashnessie?

13 Who narrowly won a seat in the Scottish parliament after a recount showed a 431-vote edge over Joan Aitken?

14 In which year was the Rout of Moy?

15 In which year was Mary, Queen of Scots executed?

ANSWERS

1. 1861 2. James Clerk Maxwell 3. A fire killed 69 children 4. 1968 5. General George Wade 6. Cape Wrath 7. Dingwall 8. Sutherland 9. Fort Augustus 10. 1979 11. Highlands and Islands 12. Sutherland 13. Fergus Ewing 14. 1746 15. 1587

1 Which West Lothian village is named after the Saxon prince Edgar Atheling?

2 Pinkie House, Musselburgh, now forms part of which school?

3 Where did the MacDougalls try and fail to ambush Robert the Bruce in 1308?

4 Where, along the Edinburgh to Lauder Road, is there a magnificent five-arch bridge built by Thomas Telford?

5 Where would you find the granute quarries of Camus and Tormore?

6 On which peninsula would you find the National Trust for Scotland farm, The Burg?

7 What is the most popular team sport in Hawick?

8 Where is the Red Hose Race run?

9 The Links of Leith were the original home of which famous golf club?

10 What was the 'prettiest cathedral city', according to Daniel Defoe?

11 The name of which Argyll island means 'tidal place' in Norse?

12 With what activity was Spott Loan, East Lothian, long associated?

13 Within 3 miles, how long is the Crinan Canal?

14 Which reservoir, near Crawford, was built largely by German POWs in the First World War?

15 Carindow, Argyll, is noted for which modern mansion?

ANSWERS

1. Port Edgar 2. Loretto School 3. The Pass of Brander 4. Pathhead 5. Bunessan 6. Ardmeanach 7. Rugby 8. Carnwath 9. The Hon. Company of Edinburgh Golfers 10. Glasgow 11. Oronsay 12. Burning witches 13. 8.5 miles 14. Camps Reservoir 15. Ardkinglass House

HISTORY

1 Which king reigned twice - but for a total of only four years - at the end of the 11th century?

2 The year 1638 saw the inception of which major group?

3 In which year did Campbell of Inverawe and his followers burn the 'Bonnie Hoose o' Arlie'?

4 In which year was the Tay Bridge Disaster?

5 In 1107, who became King of Scots?

6 In the same year who became King in Lothian and Strathclyde?

7 In which year was Charles II crowned?

8 Where did the coronation take place?

9 Norman soldiers killed how many Scots at the Battle of the Standard?

10 Where did the battle take place?

11 Which Scottish king was defeated?

12 In which year were the 'Five Articles of Perth' imposed on the Presbyterian Church in Scotland?

13 What did these Articles aim to do?

14 Where did William Smith form the Boy's Brigade in 1883?

15 The Battle of Tippermuir took place in which year?

ANSWERS

1. Donald Ban 2. The National Covenant 3. 1640 4. 1879 5. Alexander I 6. David I 7. 1651 8. Scone (the last coronation there) 9. 10,000 10. Northallerton 11. David I 12. 1618 13. Bring the Scottish Church in line with the English 14. Glasgow 15. 1644

1 Who became caretaker leader of the SDP in 1987 when David Owen resigned the leadership?

2 From which Rod Stewart album is *Sailing* taken (not that Rod Stewart's Scottish)?

3 Which was the first Chamber of Commerce in Britain?

4 In which year was it founded?

5 Which folk musician is the driving force behind the Boys of The Lough?

6 What instrument does he play?

7 In which county would you find Lord Pitsligo's Cave?

8 Where and what is the D.F.R?

9 Isle Ornsay, on Skye, takes its name from whose chapel on an adjacent island?

10 How many times did Sean Connery play James Bond?

11 How many of the Cuillin Hills are Munros?

12 The name Tobermory is associated with a character in which children's TV programme of the 1970s?

13 Who identified himself as Prince Charles Edward Stuart at Ceannaroc Bridge, Inverness-shire, in 1746, thereby allowing the Prince to escape?

14 When was the Act proscribing Highland dress repealed?

15 Which Glasgow-based band released their debut album *Young Team* in 1997?

ANSWERS

1. Robert Maclennan 2. *Atlantic Crossing* 3. Glasgow 1783 4. 5. Aly Bain 6. Fiddle 7. Aberdeenshire 8. The Dounreay Fast Reactor 9. Saint Oran 10. seven 11. fifteen 12. 'The Wombles' 13. Roderick Mackenzie 14. 1785 15. Mogwai

TV & ENTERTAINMENT

1 Who was the first Scottish female pop star to appear behind the Iron Curtain?

2 Sean Connery made a 1978 film about what type of astronomical object?

3 Who is the lead singer with Texas?

4 What was Wet Wet Wet's debut album called?

5 What office was held by the main character in *Sutherland's Law*?

6 What links Raymond Chandler's hard-bitten private eye Philip Marlowe with a Scottish pop group of the 1970s?

7 Who played Sir Lancelot Spratt in a series of 'Doctor' films?

8 Which Glasgow band was formed in the early 80s by Justin Currie and Iain Harvie?

9 What was the name of Del Amitri's first album?

10 Which band's lead singer is Elizabeth Frazer?

11 Which band had a Top 10 hit with 'Rip It Up' in 1982?

12 Who sang the 'Caravan Song', a chart hit for seven weeks in 1980?

13 What was Sean Connery's last film as James Bond?

14 Which famous Tina Turner album title track did Mark Knopfler write?

15 Which group asked 'Why' in a 1984 number six hit?

ANSWERS

1. Lulu 2. Meteor 3. Sharleen Spiteri 4. 'Popped In, Souled Out' 5. Procurator Fiscal 6. Most of the Marlowe novels took place in the Los Angeles district of Bay City 7. James Robertson Justice 8. Del Amitri 9. Del Amitri 10. Cocteau Twins 11. Orange Juice 12. Barbara Dickson 13. *Never Say Never Again* 14. 'Private Dancer' 15. Bronski Beat

1 Whom did Stephen Hendry defeat in the semi-final of the 1999 World Snooker Championship?

2 How much was Christian Dailly's move from Derby County to Blackburn Rovers worth in 1998?

3 What position does Dailly play?

4 Where, and in what year, did Mark Hayes score a record 62 at the Open?

5 Who was the oldest player ever to make an international debut?

6 Against which team did he play in this match?

7 Which English team did Kenny Dalglish manage after leaving the Liverpool job?

8 To which team did Dalglish move after leaving there?

9 Which Scot won the men's 400 m athletics gold in the 1908 Olympics?

10 Within one second, what was his time?

11 What was unusual about his victory?

12 Who holds the record for most appearances for Celtic?

13 Who holds the record for most goals scored in a single season in Britain?

14 In which season did he achieve this total?

15 In how many games did he manage this feat?

ANSWERS

1. Ronnie O'Sullivan 2. £5.35 million 3. Centre-half 4. Turnberry (1977) 5. Ronnie Simpson (1967: aged 36) 6. England 7. Blackburn Rovers 8. Newcastle United 9. Wyndham Halswelle 10. 50.0 seconds 11. It was a walkover 12. Alex McNair (548) 13. James Smith for Ayre United 14. 1927-8 15. 38

PEOPLE

31

1 Medical and religious opposition failed to stop the development of which advance pioneered by Sir James Young Simpson?

2 Under what pen-name did Neil Munro write the Para Handy stories?

3 William Smellie published the first edition of which famous title in 1768?

4 Which Dundee-born missionary was known as 'Great Mother' by the Nigerians?

5 Which position did Charles Piazzi Smyth (1819-1900) hold?

6 Which Edinburgh tradition did he initiate?

7 In what year was Muriel Spark born?

8 Which singer was known for the song 'Ye Canna Shove Yer Granny Off a Bus'?

9 Thomas Telford was born in which county?

10 The Silurian and Devonian geological systems are associated with which 19th-century geologist?

11 Where would you find a famous waterfall named after this geologist?

12 Where would you find a famous river named after this geologist?

13 Which Indian-born Scot was the architect of Coventry Cathedral?

14 With which field of learning was Dugald Stewart (1753-1828) involved?

15 Who founded the US National Parks System?

ANSWERS

1. Chloroform 2. Hugh Foulis 3. *Encyclopaedia Britannica* 4. Mary Slessor 5. Astronomer Royal for Scotland 6. The One o'clock Gun 7. 1918 8. Andy Stewart 9. Dumfriesshire 10. Sir Roderick Impey Murchison 11. Uganda: the Murchison Falls 12. Australia: the Murchison River 13. Sir Basil Spence 14. Moral philosophy 15. John Muir

1 What are the three estates depicted in *Ane Satyre of the Thrie Estaits*?

2 Before James V's marriage to whom was this play first performed?

3 With what literary style was the work of Annie S Swan associated?

4 In which Scott novel would you encounter the Laird of Dumbiedikes?

5 Which Latin scholar and one-time confidant of Mary, Queen of Scots became Moderator of the General Assembly of the Church of Scotland?

6 Who wrote the *Beside the Bonnie Brier Bush* in 1894?

7 The title *Beside the Bonnie Brier Bush* is taken from a poem by whom?

8 Whose wife was the noted translator Willa Anderson?

9 What does 'quair' mean in the title of the trilogy *A Scots Quair*?

10 Who wrote *Juan in America*, published in 1931?

11 Who wrote *Hunger March* in 1934?

12 Who described the 'Caledonian antisyzgy'?

13 What was the 'Caledonian antisyzgy'?

14 The poet William Drummond of Hawthornden was a friend of which English poet and playwright?

15 Mary, Queen of Scots, was a prolific writer. How many languages could she speak?

ANSWERS

1. Clergy, nobility and craftsmen 2. Mary of Guise-Lorraine 3. The 'Kailyard School' 4. *Heart of Midlothian* 5. George Buchanan 6. Ian Maclaren 7. Robert Burns 8. Edwin Muir 9. A collection of pages 10. Eric Linklater 11. Dot Allan 12. Hugh MacDiarmid 13. The 'zig-zag of contradictions at the heart of Scottish identity 14. Ben Jonson 15. Six

GENERAL KNOWLEDGE

1   Where did a football stadium collapse in 1902, killing 20 people and injuring 200?

2   In which year did James Young Simpson develop anaesthesia?

3   Where was the liner *Queen Mary* launched?

4   In which year was it launched?

5   Who opened the Forth Road Bridge in 1964?

6   Who opened the Tay Road Bridge in 1966?

7   Who conceived of the idea of creating the Aviemore Centre in 1965?

8   Who is the MSP for Inverness, Nairn and Lochaber?

9   Which family are known as the Lords Lovat?

10 Which mountaineer and writer comiled the *Highland Landscape* for the National Trust for Scotland?

11 In which year were the 'Five Articles of Perth' proclaimed?

12 What was the name of the 1770 programme to transform the Clyde into an industrial river?

13 Where did 69 children die in a cinema fire in 1929?

14 How was wearing of the kilt punishable in the 18th century?

15 In which year was the National Covenant formed?

ANSWERS

1   Which agricultural machinery was introduced to Scotland at Whittinghame, East Lothian, in 1932?

2   The 17th-century Hawes Inn, mentioned in Scott's *The Antiquary* and Stevenson's *Kidnapped,* is in which port?

3   Which Burns heroine is commemorated with a statue in Dunoon?

4   In which resort is 'Granny Rempock's Stone'?

5   On which Argyll island did Samuel Johnson write *Insula Sanctii Kenethi*?

6   'The Camp' in Motherwell dates back to which era?

7   Where was Lauder Ha?

8   Along which river is the 'Tail of the Bank'?

9   The weavers of which town sent an address to Abraham Lincoln supporting him during the US Civil War?

10   Port Ellen was created in which year?

11   The popular angling village of Taynuilt lies on which loch?

12   Scaranish is the only township on which island?

13   What lies at the southern end of Cowal?

14   The last what took place in Auchtertool on 26 March 1822?

15   Where was the first church built in Scotland after the Reformation?

ANSWERS

1. The combine harvester 2. South Queensferry 3. 'Highland Mary' 4. Gourock 5. Inch Kenneth 6. Roman 7. Strathlaven 8. Clyde 9. Newmilns 10. 1821 11. Etive 12. Tiree 13. Toward 14. Scotland's last recognised duel 15. Burntisland

255

HISTORY

1   At which battle was Macbeth killed?

2   In which year did this take place?

3   Who succeeded Macbeth?

4   Lowland 'Adventurers' were granted the Isle of Lewis in which year?

5   In which year was the Crofter's Act passed?

6   When did the National Gallery of Scotland open?

7   What did Magnus Barefoot claim in 1098?

8   In which year was the Gowrie Conspiracy?

9   What year is usually given as the official ending of the Highland Clearances?

10 Who defeated troops of Mary, Queen of Scots in the Battle of Langside in 1568?

11 By how much were Mary's troops outnumbered?

12 General Leslie's Parliamentary troops massacred which garrison in 1647?

13 In which battle did Malcolm Canmore die?

14 In which year did this battle take place?

15 Where was a surviving ship from the Spanish Armada sunk in 1588?

ANSWERS

1. Lumphanan 2. 1057 3. Malcolm Canmore 4. 1598 5. 1886 6. 1859 7. The Western Isles 8. 1600 9. 1854 10. Moray 11. Ten to one (45,000 vs 4,500) 12. Dunaverty 13. Alnwick 14. 1093 15. Tobermory

1 What are John Burgess, John MacLean and Terry Tully all well known as?

2 St Mary's Chapel, near Peterculter, Aberdeenshire, is associated with which two crusading orders of knights?

3 What do the letters P.F.R. refer to at Dounreay?

4 Who composed *Land of The Mountain and The Flood?*

5 Who composed *See the Conquering Hero Comes?*

6 About whom did the title refer?

7 What are 'Groatie Buckies'?

8 In which Sutherland resort is there a monument to the 'Great Plough'?

9 Why did Queen Victoria not buy Ardverikie House in Laggan and make it her Highland base instead of Bamoral?

10 'Johnnie Notions' was a weaver, clock-repairer, blacksmith and bone-setter who became famous for his inoculations during a smallpox epiedmic of 1770. Where?

11 Where is the headquarters of the Clan Gunn Society?

12 What was the 'feileadh mor'?

13 How big was the 'feileadh mor'?

14 Dalcross is the airport for which population base?

15 In which year was the Highland Light Infantry raised?

ANSWERS

1. Bagpipe players 2. Knights Templars and Knights of St John of Jerusalem 3. Prototype Fast Reactor 4. Hamish MacCunn 5. Handel 6. The Duke of Cumberland 7. European cowrie shells collected by John o' Groats 8. Lairg 9. The rain never stopped during her visit 10. Eshaness, Shetland 11. Latheron, Caithness 12. A generous length of tartan cloth worn over the shoulders and belted at the waist 13. 16 feet long and 5 feet wide 14. Inverness 15. 1777

TV & ENTERTAINMENT

1   Which song title links the Beatles with Deacon Blue?

2   Who was the first artist to have US top 5 hits in the Pop, Country, R&B, Dance and Adult Contemporary charts?

3   In which film does Sean Connery play the medieval monk-detective William Baskerville?

4   What was Fairground Attraction's follow-up single to their hit 'Perfect'?

5   What was Sean Connery's last film as James Bond before Roger Moore took over?

6   Who had a number three hit in 1988 with 'Somewhere in My Heart'?

7   The 1952 novel *Adventures in Two Worlds* gave rise to which radio and television series?

8   Who was the author of the novel?

9   True or false – Mike Scott of The Waterboys was born in Scotland?

10 Which song did China Crisis take to number nine in the charts in 1984?

11 Who went to number four in 1974 with 'All Of Me Loves All Of You'?

12 What was the name of the band formed by Dave Stewart and Annie Lennox before the Eurythmics?

13 Who was the lead singer with Orange Juice?

14 Which event of 1870 inspired the title of the group the Communards?

15 What was their first hit, which went to number one?

ANSWERS

1. 'Twist and Shout' 2. Sheena Easton 3. *The Name of the Rose* 4. 'Find My love'
5. *Diamonds Are Forever* 6. Aztec Camera 7. 'Doctor Finlay's Casebook' 8. Archibald Joseph
Cronin 9. True - he was born in Edinburgh 10. 'Wishful Thinking' 11. Bay City Rollers
12. The Tourists 13. Edwyn Collins 14. The establishment of the Paris Commune
15. 'Don't Leave Me This Way'

SPORT

1   Where, and in what year, did Isao Aoki score a record 62 at the Open?

2   In what year did Yvonne Murray win a Commonwealth Games gold medal for the 10,000 metres?

3   What was her time?

4   Who was the first Scottish football player to win 100 caps?

5   In which year did Ian St John score the winning goal in an English FA Cup final?

6   In which year did Ian Porterfield score the winning goal in an English FA Cup final?

7   Who was the last Scot to have won an Olympic gold medal?

8   Which team had the youngest-ever half-back line in Scottish football?

9   What were their names and ages?

10 Who was the youngest-ever Scot to be capped in football?

11 How old was Ronnie Simpson when he became the youngest player in the Scottish League in 1946?

12 Tom Imrie won a Commonwealth Games gold medal for boxing in which year?

13 At what weight was he boxing?

14 In which event did A Robertson win an Olympic gold in 1980?

15 In which year did the Old Course at St Andrews begin charging green fees?

ANSWERS

1. Muirfield (1980) 2. 1994 3. 31:56.97 4. Kenny Dalglish (1986) 5. 1965 6. 1973 7. Alan Wells (1980) 8. Hibernian (1956) 9. Bobby Nicol (18), Jackie Plenderleith (17) and Pat Hughes (17) 10. John Lambie (17 years old in 1886) 11. Fifteen 12. 1970 13. Light middleweight 14. 3-mile race 15. 1913

PEOPLE

1　Which Scot was head of the US Secret Service in 1861-2?

2　Where was Lord Reith born?

3　In which year did he become an MP?

4　What name is given to Sir John Steell's statue of the Duke of Wellington outside Register House in Edinburgh?

5　Under whom was William Whitelaw Deputy Prime Minister?

6　In which newspaper did Oor Wullie appear?

7　Which Roy Williamson song is an unofficial anthem of Scotland?

8　Williamson formed half of which Scottish folk band?

9　Which East Lothian native became president of Princeton University in the United States and signed the Declaration of Indepence?

10　Who was known as Michael Wylie (Machiavelli) in the 16th century, because of his subtle negotiating skills?

11　Which Protestant reformer is commemorated by a famous arch in Dundee, where he used to preach?

12　Where was racing driver Jackie Stewart born?

13　Who sued Aberdeen officials for slave trading in the 18th century?

14　Which son of a famous artist started a foundry business and pioneered the use of steam-powered tools?

15　Which artist of the 18th and 19th centuries is famous for his portaits of Sir Walter Scott and David Hume?

ANSWERS

1. Allan Pinkerton 2. Stonehaven 3. 1940 4. 'The Iron Duke in bronze by Steell' 5. Margaret Thatcher 6. *Sunday Post* 7. 'Flower of Scotland' 8. The Corries 9. John Witherspoon 10. William Maitland 11. George Wishart 12. Dumbarton 13. Peter Williamson 14. James Nasmyth 15. Sir Henry Raeburn

MUSIC & LITERATURE

1. Which poem by Sir Walter Scott concerns the maid Gwyneth?

2. Which novel did Burns say he prized next to the Bible?

3. With what literary style was the work of S R Crockett associated?

4. Who wrote the grim account of rural life *The House with the Green Shutters?*

5. Which author tried to enlist in the First World War but was refused because of his age (62)?

6. Of which political party was he co-founder?

7. Of which political party was he also first president?

8. Whose sister was the writer O. Douglas?

9. What was her real name?

10. How old was the poet Robert Ferguson when he died?

11. In which year did he die?

12. In which language did he write?

13. Which English author was a close friend of Catherine Carswell and the subject of a memoir written by her?

14. In which Scott novel would you meet 'Wandering Willie'?

15. Following the downfall of Mary, Queen of Scots, who published a denunciation of her which included some of her verses as evidence of her adultery?

ANSWERS

1. The Bridal of Triermain 2. *The Man of Feeling* 3. The Kailyard School 4. George Douglas Brown 5. Robert Bontine Cunninghame Graham 6. Scottish Labour Party 7. Scottish National Party 8. John Buchan 9. Anna 10. 24 11. 1774 12. Scots 13. D H Lawrence 14. *Redgauntlet* 15. George Buchanan

261

GENERAL KNOWLEDGE

1 When did James Watt build the first steam engine with a separate condensor?

2 What town is the headquarters of the Ross and Cromarty District?

3 Who is the MSP for Moray?

4 In which county would you find Loch Veyatie?

5 Sir Reginald de Moravia died fighting whom at Embo, Sutherland?

6 How did Lord Lovat part with his newly bought estate of Fort Augustus in 1867?

7 Dulsie Bridge passes over a gorge of which river?

8 Which MSP has the nickname 'the gannet'?

9 In which battle of 1690 were General Buchan's sleeping Highlanders surprised, and more than 300 of them killed?

10 Which transport charge figured prominently in the poltical in-fighting that preceded the Labour-Lib Dem coalition in the Scottish Parliament?

11 With what sport was Lady Heathcoat Amory associated?

12 What is, or was, the D.E.R.E.?

13 In which year were Penal Statutes against Clan Gregor repealed?

14 In which century did George Dempster, the 'improver', live?

15 After whom is the Ross Ice Shelf, Antarctica, named?

ANSWERS

1. 1776 2. Dingwall 3. Margaret Ewing 4. Sutherland 5. The Danes 6. By seeing that a Benedictine abbey and school were built there 7. Findhorn 8. Donald Dewar 9. The Battle of the Haughs of Cromdale 10. The Skye Bridge toll 11. Golf 12. The Dounreay Experimental Reactor Establishment 13. 1775 14. 18th-century 15. Sir James Clark Ross

1   Where is Constantine's Grave?

2   Which island is sometimes called the 'Iona of the East'?

3   Who described the local trades of Kirkcaldy in *Free Fishers*?

4   Which milestone book on economics was written in Kirkcally in 1776?

5   Which Prime Minister made many speeches at the Masonic Hall in Ladybank?

6   Panmure House, Forfarshire, was a seat of which earls?

7   Which Scottish railway station is unofficially reckoned to be the most windswept in the UK?

8   What is the most northerly town in Fife?

9   A monument to which regiment stands in Aberfeldy?

10 Bishop Henry Wardlaw is associated with the founding of which seat of higher learning?

11 Where are the twin volcanoes *Erebus* and *Terror*?

12 After which Scottish explorer's two ships are they named?

13 From which university was a biblical scholar dismissed for heresy in the 19th century?

14 Who was this scholar?

15 Where is Sir Walter Scott buried?

ANSWERS

1. Crail 2. Inchcolm 3. John Buchan 4. *The Wealth of Nations* 5. H H Asquith 6. Dalhousie 7. Leuchars Junction 8. Tayport 9. Black Watch 10. St Andrews University 11. Antarctica 12. Sir James Clark Ross 13. Aberdeen 14. William Robertson-Smith, who questioned the Old Testament 15. Dryburgh Abbey

HISTORY

1 Which two rulers joined forces to defeat a Northumbrian army at the Battle of Carham?

2 In which year did this battle take place?

3 The year 1557 saw the formation of which secret Protestant group?

4 Where was the famous divine and humanist Thomas Chalmers born in 1780?

5 When did the Sutherland Clearances begin?

6 In which year did Robert Thomson invent the pneumatic tyre?

7 William the Conqueror received homage from whom in 1073 after William's victory?

8 Which two Highland regiments were founded in 1794?

9 In which year was the Glasgow Chamber of Commerce founded?

10 James VI died in what year?

11 In which year were the infamous Witchcraft Acts passed by Mary, Queen of Scots?

12 Whom did she marry two years later?

13 What position was held by MacKinnon, who died in 1550?

14 What was the name of the conflict that began in 1639?

15 At the end of which century was the reign of Donald Ban?

ANSWERS

1. Malcolm II and Owen of Strathclyde 2. 1018 3. Covenant 4. Anstruther, Fife 5. 1807 6. 1845 7. Malcolm III 8. Argyll and Sutherland Highlanders and Gordon Highlanders 9. 1783 10. 1625 11. 1563 12. Henry Darnley 13. Last abbot of Iona 14. The First Bishops' War 15. 11th.

1 In which year were the Gordon Highlanders raised?

2 How often a year does the High Court of Justiciary sit at Inverness?

3 Which is the oldest authenticated tower-house on the mainland of Scotland?

4 Which two famous people stayed at Pitcaple Castle in 1650?

5 Where would you find the islands of East and West Burra?

6 In which county would you find the Muckle Ordeal Stone of Auchmaliddie?

7 How many miles long, within 20 miles, was the Maiden Head to John o' Groats Race?

8 How many miles long, within 50 miles, was the Land's End to John o' Groats Race?

9 Loch Sionascaig is wholly surrounded by which nature reserve?

10 Hermaness is the northern tip of which island?

11 Where does the River Dee have its source?

12 Which passenger from the *Doutelle* spent seven days at Borrodale House, Inverness-shire?

13 In which county would you find the township of Mellon Urdigle?

14 What forms the southern tip of Shetland?

15 Which landmark, rather than John o' Groats, is the most northerly point of mainland on Great Britain?

ANSWERS

1. 1794 2. twice 3. The Castle of Dunnideer 4. The Duke of Montrose on the way to his execution and Charles II on his way to be crowned 5. Shetland 6. Aberdeenshire 7. 280 miles 8. 873 miles 9. Inverpolly 10. Unst 11. The Pools of Dee 12. Bonnie Prince Charlie 13. Ross and Cromarty 14. Jarlshof 15. Dunnet Head

TV & ENTERTAINMENT

1 Who had a hit with 'There is a Mountain' in 1967?

2 What was the only chart hit, in 1986, for Hipsway?

3 Which title did the Co-op Welfare Society (Glasgow) win in both 1990 and 1996?

4 Which Scottish band's first album, released in 1989, was called 'Southside'?

5 Frankie Millar had one chart hit, reaching number six in 1978. What was its title?

6 What was Sean Connery's last film as James Bond?

7 How many years had elapsed since Sean Connery had first played James Bond?

8 Who went to number six with 'Labour of Love' in 1987?

9 Which Shakespearean question did B A Robertson ponder in 1980?

10 Of which band was Billy MacKenzie the lead singer?

11 In which two years were all of Gallacher and Lyle's chart hits?

12 Who was the lead singer of The Rezillos?

13 'Hallelujah Freedom' was a top ten hit for whom in 1972?

14 Who was the lead singer of Jethro Tull?

15 Which instrument does this singer also play?

ANSWERS

1. Donovan 2. 'The Honeythief' 3. British Brass Band Champions 4. 'Texas 5. 'Darlin'' 6. *Never Say Never Again* 7. 21 8. Hue and Cry 9. 'To be or not to be' 10. The Associates 11. 1976 and 1977 12. Fay Fife 13. Junior Campbell 14. Ian Anderson 15. Flute

SPORT

1 Who won the first Open Golf Championship in 1860?

2 On which course was it played?

3 What is the highest number of goals scored by a British football team in a Professional League season?

4 Over how many matches did they achieve this total?

5 Where was the first inter-club golfing match held?

6 In what year did the match take place?

7 In which year did Alan Wells win a Commonwealth gold in the 100 metres with a time of 10.05 seconds?

8 Why was Wells's time not a new record?

9 In which year was Kenny Dalglish born?

10 In which year did Alex McNair first appear for Celtic?

11 In which year did Alex McNair last appear for Celtic?

12 Which Turkish team has Graeme Souness managed?

13 To which English club did Souness move upon leaving Turkey?

14 In which year did the team (swimming) of Gordon, Girvan and McDowall set a Commonwealth Records record of 3:51 for the 3 X 110 medley relay?

15 Where, and in what year, did Greg Norman score a record 62 at the Open?

ANSWERS

1. Tom Morris 2. Prestwick 3. Raith Rovers: 142 in 1937–8 4. 34 matches 5. Bruntsfield Golf Club: Edinburgh Burgess Golfing Society against Bruntsfield Golf Club 6. 1818 7. 1982 8. It was wind-assisted 9. 1951 10. 1904 11. 1925 12. Galatasaray 13. Southampton 14. 1954 15. Turnberry (1986)

1 Which Scottish geologist predicted the discovery of gold in Australia?

2 Which Edinburgh society painter was a friend of Adam Smith and David Hume?

3 Who was the first explorer to cross Australia from North to South?

4 Which 18th-century Aberdeenshire native was known as 'Indian Peter'?

5 Why was he so known?

6 Which famous landscape painter also produced one of the most famous portraits of Robert Burns?

7 Who encouraged this painter when he was still an apprentice coach-painter in Edinburgh?

8 Who developed the process of refining oil in the 19th century?

9 Where did he develop a pioneering oil works?

10 In what year did Princess Margaret divorce?

11 Where was Lady Elizabeth Bowes-Lyon born?

12 Where was she brought up?

13 Who is credited with inventing the decimal point?

14 Which 19th-century Aberdeen biblical scholar was charged with heresy after questioning parts of the Old Testament?

15 What relation was Elizabeth I of England to Mary, Queen of Scots?

ANSWERS

1. Sir Roderick Impey Murchison 2. Allan Ramsay 3. John McDougall Stuart 4. Peter Williamson 5. He was captured by Cherokees 6. Alexander Nasmyth 7. Allan Ramsay 8. James Young 9. Oil Shales of West Lothian 10. 1978 11. London 12. Glamis Castle 13. John Napier 14. William Robertson-Smith 15. Cousin

1 Whose tranlsation of Blind Harry's *Wallace* was accepted as the norm in the 18th century?

2 Who coined the term 'Lallans' to decribe the Scots tongue?

3 Who revived the term in the 20th century?

4 Who wrote the long poem 'The City of Dreadful Night'?

5 In what year was this poem published?

6 In which Scott novel would you find Tillietudlem Castle

7 With what literary style was the work of William Sharp associated?

8 Under what pseudonym did Sharp write many of his works?

9 The poet James Ballantine contributed to which now-derided series of anthologies?

10 How did the apocalyptic writer John Davidson die?

11 In which year did he die?

12 In which Scott novel would you encounter Sir William Ashton?

13 Where was Scott born?

14 What was the 'Kailyard School', associated with the novels of J M Barrie?

15 The French poet Pierre de Ronsard was a friend of which Scottish monarch?

ANSWERS

1. William Hamilton 2. Robert Burns 3. Hugh MacDiarmid 4. James Thomson 5. 1874 6. *Castle Dangerous* 7. 'Celtic Twilight' 8. Fiona MacLeod 9. The 'Whistle-binkie' anthologies 10. Suicide 11. 1909 12. *Bride of Lammermoor* 13. Edinburgh 14. Sentimental fiction 15. Mary, Queen of Scots

GENERAL KNOWLEDGE

1   Within 3 percentage points, what was the electoral turnout for the first elections to the Scottish Parliament in May 1999?

2   Dingwall's name comes from which Norse word meaning Parliament?

3   Robert Munro, the 'black baron', died fighting for which European monarch in 1633?

4   Which party gained its first UK parliamentary seat by winning more than 22,000 votes in the Lothians under proportional representation?

5   What is the name of this party's MSP?

6   With which regiment were the Seaforth Highlanders amalgamated in 1963?

7   What was the name of the new regiment?

8   How many seats did the SNP achieve in the 1999 Scottish Parliamentary elections?

9   What had been SNP leader Alex Salmond's target for the elections?

10 Why was a deep-water diving school founded in Fort William in 1975?

11 What is the official Debrett's title of the first Presiding Officer of the Scottish Parliament?

12 Who built the original Fort George, Inverness-shire?

13 How many members of the Ewing family were elected as MSPs in May 1999?

14 Who were they - and what is their inter-relationship?

15 Which is reckoned to be the most northerly first-class golf course in the world?

ANSWERS

1. 59 per cent 2. 'Thing' 3. Gustavus of Sweden 4. The Green Party 5. Robin Harper 6. Queen's Own Cameron Highlanders 7. Queen's Own Highlanders 8. 36 9. 40 seats 10. To train divers for North Sea oil work 11. Lord Steel of Aikwood 12. General Wade 13. Three 14. Winnie Ewing, her son Fergus and his wife Margaret 15. Royal Dornoch

PLACES

1   Who built the Augustinian abbey at Inchcolm?

2   At which university was Joseph Black Professor of Anatomy and Chemistry?

3   What was the name of the experiment in social engineering founded by David Dale in 1785?

4   After whom is the Ross Dependency in Antarctica named?

5   Will Fyffe, famous for the song 'I Belong to Glasgow', was actually born where?

6   Which Scot found his way to the Magnetic South Pole in 1909?

7   Where was the novelist Neil Gunn born in 1891?

8   Where was the famous Scots Kirk, of Second World War fame?

9   The Mearns were a literary inspiration for which writer?

10 Of which American colony did Glasgow-born Robert Dinwiddie become lieutenant-governor?

11 Where did the famous botanist David Douglas die?

12 Where could you find the Burrell Collection of art and antiques?

13 Which Principal of St Andrews and Edinburgh Universities was a pioneer in the study of polarised light?

14 Where did Sir Robert Sibbald found an important botanical garden?

15 Which abbey did Queen Margaret re-found?

ANSWERS

1. Alexander I 2. Glasgow 3. New Lanark 4. Sir James Clark Ross 5. Dundee 6. Alistair Forbes-Mackay 7. Caithness 8. Paris 9. Lewis Grassic Gibbon 10. Virginia 11. Hawaii 12. Pollock Park, Glasgow 13. Sir David Brewster 14. Edinburgh 15. Iona

HISTORY

1 Which king's reign lasted from 878 to 889?

2 In which year was Cardinal Beaton murdered?

3 The Second Bishops' War began in which year?

4 Which important battle took place in 977?

5 In which year did Mary, Queen of Scots first marry?

6 Who was her husband?

7 In which century did King Indulf reign?

8 Which clan massacred the Lamonts at Dunoon in 1646?

9 What year is cited as the official start of the Highland Clearances?

10 Who reigned from 962 to 966?

11 What did this king's name translate to in English?

12 Whom did Malcolm II kill to become king?

13 What name was given to the meeting between Charles I and three Scots commissioners in 1647?

14 Where did the meeting take place?

15 What was agreed at this meeting?

ANSWERS

1. Eochaid 2. 1546 3. 1640 4. Luncarty 5. 1558 6. Francis II *Dauphin* of France 7. Tenth 8. The Campbells 9. 1785 10. Dubh 11. Black 12. Kenneth III 13. The 'Engagement' 14. The Isle of Wight 15. Charles agreed to promote Presbyterianism in England in return for Lowland support in the Civil War

1 Which exiled French king helped fund the building of St Thomas's Catholic church of St Thomas in Keith, Banffshire?

2 In which year was it built (within ten)?

3 Charles II danced under a thorn tree at Pitcaple Castle in 1650. Who planted it?

4 Over which loch does the Black Spout tower?

5 In which country would you find Pluscarden Abbey?

6 Where, in 1881 did Arthur Forbes erect a famous cairn?

7 How was the 17th-century Sir Robert Gordon of Moray known?

8 In which county is Bealach nam Ba, one of Scotland's highest roads?

9 Which town lost out in importance to Geantown-on-Spey after being the scene of a market brawl in the 17th century?

10 How was General Sir Hector Macdonald (1853-1903) known to his troops?

11 Sir Francis Chichester unveiled a plaque dedicated to whom in the Kincardineshire village of Inverbervie in 1969?

12 Which famous ship had been designed by the person so honoured in 1969?

13 In which Moray port was the first 'Zulu' boat built in 1879?

14 Who, according to a hotly debated story, betrayed Montrose for the blood money of £25,000 after finding the great soldier wandering the moors?

15 During his Highland Tour, Doctor Johnson was annoyed when asked by locals whether he was one of the Johnsons of where?

ANSWERS

1. Charles X 2. 1830 3. His great-grandmother Mary, Queen of Scots 4. Lochnagar 5. Moray 6. Culloden Moor 7. The 'Warlock Laird' 8. Ross and Cromarty 9. Cromdale 10. 'Fighting Mac' 11. Hercules Linton 12. The *Cutty Sark* 13. Lossiemouth 14. MacLeod of Assynt 15. Ardnamurchan

TV & ENTERTAINMENT

1 Who starred in both *The Great Escape* and *One of Our Spies Is Missing?*

2 Who had a hit in 1975 with 'The Old Rugged Cross', her only chart entry?

3 Which band had a hit in 1988 with *Somewhere in My Heart?*

4 Who was the Bay City Rollers lead singer?

5 Which was the only Agatha Christie adaptation in which Sean Connery starred?

6 *Land Of The Mountain And The Flood* was the name of the signature tune for which TV series? .

7 Who was the star of *Sutherland's Law?*

8 What links Billy Connolly with Tammy Wynnette?

9 Which group had a 1971 hit with 'Malt and Barley Blues'?

10 Which Edinburgh landmark features in the title of a 1980 song by Gerry Rafferty?

11 Which Beatles song gave Marmalade a number one hit in 1968?

12 To which Bee Gee was Lulu married between 1969 and 1973?

13 Who had a hit with 'Word Up' in 1994?

14 Which 18th-century agricultural innovator unwittingly gave his name to a rock band of the 1960s?

15 The actress Iona Skye is the daughter of which 1960s folk/rock singer?

ANSWERS

1. David McCallum 2. Ethna Campbell 3. Aztec Camera 4. Les McKeown 5. *Murder on the Orient Express* 6. 'Sutherland's Law' 7. Iain Cuthbertson 8. Both had hits with 'D.I.V.O.R.C.E.' 9. McGuinness Flint 10. 'Royal Mile' 11. 'O-bla-di-o-bla-da' 12. Maurice Gibb 13. Gun 14. Jethro Tull 15. Donovan

SPORT

1. What was the song title of the Scottish World Cup Squad's 1982 hit?

2. In which year did David Wilkie first win a gold at the Commonwealth Games?

3. For which event did he win the gold?

4. In which other event at the same Games did he set a new Games record of 2:10:11?

5. What was Graeme Souness's first managerial posting?

6. In which year did Richard Noble first become the 'fastest man on earth'?

7. How -and where - did he achieve this title?

8. In which year did he achieve this title once more?

9. What was the name of the team he led on this second occasion?

10. Which is the only football club to have won the European Cup and two senior domestic cups in one season?

11. Scotland were the first winners of the Rous Cup: in which year?

12. In which year did Celtic notch its thirtieth Scottish FA Cup victory?

13. Who was the first Scot to play for a Women's World Cup-winning team in football?

14. Which team did she represent?

15. In which year did the Old Course at St Andrews adopt 18 holes as the norm?

ANSWERS

1. 'We Have a Dream' 2. 1974 3. 200m backstroke 4. 200m individual medley 5. Rangers 6. 1983 7. By breaking the land speed record in the Nevada desert 8. 1997 9. Thrust SSC 10. Celtic (1967) 11. 1985 12. 1995 13. Rose Reilly 14. Italy 15. 1764

PEOPLE

1 In which US city did Allan Pinkerton form his first detective agency?

2 What was its first success?

3 Which of Robert William Thomson's inventions was deemed too expensive for practical use?

4 Which agricultural invention is also credited to Thomson?

5 Who coined the term 'Americanism'?

6 Was William Whitelaw ever Foreign Secretary?

7 Who 'discovered' Victoria Falls?

8 Where was Viscount William Whitelaw raised?

9 Who created 'Desperate Dan'?

10 What is the full name of Princess Margaret's former husband, Lord Snowdon?

11 In what year was George Wishart burnt at the stake?

12 In what year did Robert Adam die?

13 By which name was the noted mathematician and physicist William Thomson (1824-1907) better known?

14 Who invented coal-gas lighting?

15 In which year did he invent it?

ANSWERS

1. Chicago 2. Solving a series of train robberies 3. The pneumatic tyre 4. A steam tractor engine 5. John Witherspoon 6. No 7. David Livingstone 8. Nairn 9. Dudley D. Watkins 10. Anthony Armstrong-Jones 11. 1546 12. 1792 13. Lord Kelvin (of Largs) 14. William Murdock 15. 1792

276

MUSIC & LITERATURE

1 Which Sir Walter Scott novel takes its name from the Edinburgh Tolbooth?

2 Which famous novelist set out orginally to be a lighhouse designer?

3 At what age did he change his mind?

4 Who coined the term 'Kailyard School'?

5 Which poet won the Queen's Gold Medal for poetry in 1986?

6 Who wrote *English Bards and Scotch Reviewers*?

7 Who was the author of *Wee Willie Winkie*?

8 Which famous character did Dr Joseph Bell inspire?

9 Who wrote the 1920 novel *Open the Door!*?

10 Which author helped 'invent' clan tartans in honour of a Royal visit to Scotland?

11 With what literary style was the work of William Black associated?

12 The poet Alexander Rodger contributed to which series of mawkish anthologies?

13 Which 19th-century critic wrote on a wide range of subjects, from anthropology to fairies?

14 Sir Walter Scott enjoyed considerable success translating literature from which language?

15 Which tutor of Mary, Queen of Scots, also taught the French writer Montaigne in Bordeaux?

ANSWERS

1. *Heart of Midlothian* 2. Robert Louis Stevenson 3. 21 4. The critic J H Millar 5. Norman McCaig 6. Lord Byron 7. William Miller 8. Sherlock Holmes 9. Catherine Carswell 10. Sir Walter Scott 11. 'Celtic Twilight' 12. The 'Whistle-Binkie' anthologies 13. Andrew Lang 14. German 15. George Buchanan

GENERAL KNOWLEDGE

1. On which river does Kirkudbright stand?

2. Where did the Battle of Tears Chapel take place in 1464?

3. This battle was part of a long-standing feud between which two families?

4. Which prominent Tory was elected to the Scottish Parliament throught the party lists for Lothian after failing to win in the first-past-the-post stage?

5. Which Westminster post had he held under the last Tory government?

6. Bidean nam Bian is the highest mountain in which county?

7. Which sportsman-laird founded Inverewe Garden in 1862?

8. Near which Sutherland township is a plaque commemorating the geologists Benjamin N. Peach and John Horne?

9. Which two rivers meet at Invershine, Sutherland?

10. Which prominent SNP official narrowly missed being elected to the Glasgow Goven constituency in the 1999 Scottish Parliamentary election?

11. In which manner was she elected as an MSP?

12. How old is she?

13. How many women were elected as MSPs in May 1999?

14. What nickname has been given to this group of MSPs?

15. What does the Glen Coe place-name Aonach Eagach mean in English?

ANSWERS

1. River Dee 2. Girnigoe Castle 3. The Gunns and the Keiths 4. Lord James Douglas-Hamilton 5. Scottish Office Minister 6. Argyll 7. Osgood Mackenzie 8. Inchnadamph 9. Oykell and Shin 10. Nicola Sturgeon 11. In the Glasgow regional lists 12. 28 13. 47 14. The 'Holyrood Wives' 15. 'Notched ridge'

1   Which Glasgow museum is named after a pioneer in obstetrics?

2   In which institution was the anatomist Dr Robert Knox working when he employed the famous body snatchers Burke and Hare?

3   Where in North America did Flora Macdonald try to enlist Scots to the British cause in the American War of Independence?

4   Where was the Canadian explorer Sir Alexander Mackenzie born?

5   At which university did three generations of the Monro family hold the Chair of Anatomy, for a period lasting 126 years?

6   In which American state did Richard Noble first become the Fastest Man on Earth, in 1983?

7   Which famous brewer was born in Alloa in 1827?

8   Tinwald, Dumfriesshire, was the birthplace of which famous financier?

9   Where are the only two round towers in Scotland?

10 What purpose did they serve?

11 Duncan's Camp, where King Duncan was said to have held court, lies near which Perthshire town?

12 Where was the poet William McGonagall born in 1830?

13 Where was the famous pirate, Captain Kidd, born?

14 Which American city honoured him for his privateering work, before he changed side and became a pirate himself?

15 Saint Mungo is known as the Apostle of where?

ANSWERS

1. Hunterian Museum 2. Edinburgh Medical School 3. North Carolina 4. Lewis 5. Edinburgh 6. Nevada 7. Dr William McEwan 8. William Paterson 9. Abernethy and Brechin 10. As protection against Viking raiders 11. Birnam 12. Edinburgh 13. Greenock 14. New York 15. Cumbria

HISTORY

34

1 What technological advance was introduced to Scotland in 1507?

2 In which year was the Solemn League and Covenant signed?

3 In which battle of 685 did Picts defeat the Angles and establish Scotland's southern border?

4 Who was their leader?

5 In which year was a major programme of road-building begun in the Highlands in the 18th century?

6 Why was this done?

7 Which king's reign lasted from 877 to 878?

8 In which year did James V's reign begin?

9 In which year was the major excavation programme known as the Clyde Trust initiated?

10 In which battle of AD 600 were 300 Edinburgh horsemen killed by the English?

11 When did Adam Smith publish *The Wealth of Nations?*

12 The insurrection of Donald Dubh took place in which year?

13 The birth of which famous Scot occurred in the same year as the major defeat at the Battle of Solway Moss?

14 Which was the year?

15 Which King of Dalriada died in 606?

ANSWERS

1. Printing 2. 1643 3. Nechtansmere 4. Brude 5. 1725 6. To make access easier for British troops 7. Aed 8. 1528 9. 1770 10. Catterick 11. 1776 12. 1503 13. Mary, Queen of Scots 14. 1542 15. Aidan

280

TRIVIA

1 Over which Aberdeenshire castle's entrance is there the inscription 'Nothing on earth remains but fame'?

2 Near which Aberdeenshire village is Tap o' Noth?

3 The Highland chief Sir Alexander Macdonald of Armadale gave Johnson and Boswell a chilly reception in 1773. How did Johnson account for his host's behaviour?

4 In which county would you find the village Monymusk?

5 Who were the 'Sobieski Stuarts'?

6 Which monarch believed their story?

7 In which Ross and Cromarty church can you see plaintive messages scrawled by villagers evicted during the Highland Clearances?

8 In which year was the New Testament first published in Gaelic?

9 Which Gaelic poet is commemorated in the clock tower of Arisaig Catholic church in Inverness-shire?

10 With which historical event is this poet associated?

11 Which flower was long known as the 'stinking willie' in Scotland?

12 The 'Memory Park' of which clan was laid out near Kinchyle, Inverness-shire?

13 In which year was Rangers Football Club founded?

14 Was Charles I born in Scotland?

15 What was Sean Connery's first film as James Bond?

ANSWERS

1. Glenbuchat Castle 2. Rhynie 3. That Macdonald had been 'tamed into insignificance' by his education at Eton 4. Aberdeenshire 5. Eccentric brothers in Inverness-shire who believed themselves to be legitimate grandsons of Charles Edward Stuart 6. Queen Victoria 7. Croick 8. 1767 9. Alasdair MacMhaigstir Alasdair 10. The Rising of 1745 11. Sweet William 12. McBain 13. 1873 14. Yes 15. *Dr No*

TV & ENTERTAINMENT

1 What was the highest that Gerry Rafferty's smash hit 'Baker Street' reached in 1978?

2 Which group had the 1970s album 'Thick As a Brick'?

3 With whom did B A Robertson duet on his 1981 hit 'Hold Me'?

4 Which pescatorian was 'Incommunicado' in 1987?

5 Who warned listeners to 'Sanctify Yourself' in 1986?

6 What was the second half of the title of the Bay City Rollers' 1974 hit 'Remember'?

7 How did this song climb in the charts?

8 Who sang a 'Love Song for a Vampire' in 1993?

9 Who played Lady Macbeth in Roman Polanski's 1971 film version of the play?

10 True or false – Mark Knopfler of Dire Straits was born in Scotland?

11 The title of which 1988 song echoed the name of the group?

12 Who starred in the comedy-drama 'The Bogey Man'?

13 Who played Jamieson Fildes in 'The Brief'?

14 Which presenter was chosen from 6000 applicants to front 'The Disney Club'?

15 Who played Dirk Mallen in the TV series 'The Mallens'?

ANSWERS

1. Number 3 2. Jethro Tull 3. Maggie Bell 4. Fish: lead singer of Marillion, which had that hit 5. Simple Minds 6. 'Sha-la-la' 7. number 6 8. Annie Lennox 9. Francesca Annis 10. True - he was born in Glasgow 11. 'Goodbye Mr Mackenzie' 12. Robbie Coltrane 13. Charles Jamieson 14. Gordon Inglis 15. David Rintoul

SPORT

1 Who was the first non-British footballer to play for a Scottish side?

2 In which year did he join the team?

3 How many goals did James McGrory score with Celtic between 1922 and 1938?

4 Who holds the women's record for racing to the summit of Ben Nevis and down again?

5 Within 5 minutes, what was her record time?

6 In which year did the R&A assume control of the rules of golf?

7 Who holds the record for most Scottish Cup winners medals?

8 How many medals did he win, and over which period overall?

9 Which two 17th-century kings were definitely recorded playing golf?

10 Which Scot scored Nottingham Forest's FA Cup-winning goal in 1981?

11 Which Egyptian played inside forward for Rangers in 1934?

12 What was Scotland's worst World Cup defeat?

13 The Egyptian goalkeeper Mustafa Mansour played for which club between 1937 and 1940?

14 Which jockey holds the British Classic Record with 14?

15 Who is Scotland's only three-time World Sculling Champion?

ANSWERS

1. Carl Hansen (Denmark, joined Rangers) 2. 1922 3. 550 4. Pauline Haworth (1984) 5. 1 hour, 43 minutes, 25 seconds 6. 1897 7. Charles Campbell of Queen's Park 8. 8 medals between 1874 and 1886 9. Charles I and James VII (II of England) 10. John Robertson 11. Mohammed Latif 12. Uruguay 7-0 (1954) 13. Queen's Park 14. Willie Carson 15. Peter Haining

PEOPLE

1. Which Cabinet Minister represents Edinburgh Central?

2. How long did Francis II, first husband of Mary, Queen of Scots, reign in France?

3. What was David Livingstone trying to discover when he died in 1873?

4. Livingstone was the first white man to travel the length of which African lake?

5. In which year did Sir James Clark Ross claim Antarctica for Queen Victoria?

6. Which temperature scale, taking absolute zero as its starting point, is named after a Scottish physicist?

7. In which century did John Duns Scotus die?

8. Which invention of Sir Robert Alexander Watson-Watt was first used extensively in the Second World War?

9. Whose catchphrase was 'Jings! Crivvens! Help ma Boab!'?

10. How old was Manny Shinwell when he died?

11. What did he nationalise in 1946?

12. In which year did boxer Jim Watt win the WBC World Lightweight title?

13. Who created 'The Broons'?

14. Who sang the title song for the film *To Sir with Love?*

15. Which Scot was instrumental in the founding of the Royal Geological Society in London?

ANSWERS

1. Alistair Darling 2. One year 3. The source of the Nile 4. Tanganyika 5. 1841 6. Kelvin Lord Kelvin *of Largs* 7. 14th 8. Radar 9. Oor Wullie 10. 102 11. The mining industry 12. 1979 13. Dudley D. Watkins 14. Lulu 15. Sir Roderick Impey Murchison

MUSIC & LITERATURE

1   Which popular Gaelic 'translation' of 1761 turned out to have been composed by the author?

2   Who was the author of this hoax?

3   George MacDonald is noted for what type of literature?

4   With what literary style was the early work of Neil Munro associated?

5   Who wrote under the pseudonym 'B.V.'?

6   Who wrote *Coral Island*?

7   In which war was the poet Ewart Alan Mackintosh killed?

8   Which now infamous book of 1899 was written by Helen Bannerman?

9   Whose account of his own crippling disease was published as *Diaries of a Dying Man*?

10   In which Scott novel would you encounter Lord Ravenswood?

11   Who edited the much-enlarged second edition of the *Encyclopaedia Britannica*?

12   What feat did this editor achieve in August 1784?

13   Which composer's best-known work is 'Land of Mountain and the Flood'?

14   Against which monarch was John Knox's *First Blast of the Trumpet Against the Monstrous Regiment of Women* aimed?

15   How did this work land Knox in trouble?

ANSWERS

1. *Ossian* 2. James Macpherson 3. Children's 4. 'Celtic Twilight' 5. James Thomson 6. R M Ballantyne 7. The First World War 8. *Little Black Sambo* 9. William Soutar 10. *Bride of Lammermoor* 11. James Tytler 12. He became Britain's first hot-air balloonist 13. Hamish MacCunn 14. Mary, Queen of Scots, 15. It could be seen as a criticism of Elizabeth I of England

GENERAL KNOWLEDGE

1   Which prominent SNP official narrowly missed being elected to the Ochill constituency in the 1999 Scottish Parliamentary election?

2   The Dutchman John de Groot gave his name to which Scottish place-name?

3   What service did he provide in the 15th-century?

4   For which party did Tasmina Ahmed-Sheik stand as an MSP candidate in Glasgow Govan?

5   Which Laggan house did Queen Victoria briefly consider buying instead of Balmoral?

6   Latherton, Caithness, is the headquarters of which clan?

7   'The Wag' is an Iron Age homestead located in which county?

8   In which county would you find the village of Lochaline?

9   Which prominent Tory was elected to the Scottish Parliament through the party lists after failing to win in the first-past-the-post vote in the Edinburgh pentlands constituency?

10 The parishoners of which Argyll village built a 'floating church' off the shore in the 19th century after their landlord refused to build a new church following the 'Disruption'?

11 Which settlement on Lewis is noted for its crucifrom setting of megaliths?

12 What type of weapons does the Royal Navy test at Kyle of Lochalsh?

13 In which county would you find Kylesku?

14 Who gave his name to the Ross Sea, Antarctica?

15 Who was Mary of Modena's famous son?

ANSWERS

1. George Reid 2. John o' Groats 3. The Orkney ferry service 4. The Conservatives 5. Ardverikie 6. Clan Gunn 7. Caithness 8. Argyll 9. David McLetchie 10. Strontian 11. Callanish 12. Torpedoes 13. Sutherland 14. Sir James Clark Ross 15. The Old Pretender

PLACES

1. Where is the Fountain Brewery?
2. In which county could you find Dull?
3. Which famous writer of folk songs died in Findo Gask in 1845?
4. Inver was the lifetime home of which famous fiddler?
5. In which county is Cambus o' May?
6. Which river flows through the Sma' Glen in Perthshire?
7. Which sandy area in Moray was once known as the 'Scottish Sahara'?
8. Near which Kincardineshire town is the Cairn o' Mount Pass?
9. Which city is headquarters of the Tayside Region?
10. In which Moray town is the Aul 'Eel ceremony held?
11. What was the original name of the Harris village now known as Leverburgh?
12. Which river has been described as being 'bright, snow-fed'?
13. Near which Perthshire town was the Battle of Dupplin fought in 1332?
14. Which Second World War hero is associated with the Scots Kirk, Paris?
15. In which other French city did he acquire his famous nickname?

ANSWERS

1. Edinburgh 2. Perthshire 3. Caroline Oliphant *Lady Nairne* 4. Neil Gow 5. Aberdeenshire 6. Almond 7. Culbin 8. Banchory 9. Dundee 10. Burghead 11. Obbe 12. The Dee 13. Forteviot 14. Donald Caskie, the 'Tartan Pimpernel' 15. Marseilles

HISTORY

1 Under whom did Celtic tribes unite in AD 84, before being defeated by the Romans?

2 How many of these Celtic soldiers died in battle?

3 In which year was James I allowed to return from captivity in England?

4 Who was appointed Commander-in-Chief in the Highlands in 1725?

5 When was the Glenturret Distillery, Scotland's oldest, founded?

6 In which year did Pict, Scot and Saxon tribes attack the Romans in London and plunder their treasures?

7 In which year was the Black Watch regiment founded?

8 The potato was introduced to the Highlands in which year?

9 Which group of people established Christianity as the religion in the Kingdom of Dalriad in about 501?

10 In which year was the University of Glasgow founded?

11 How many years earlier had the University of St Andrews been founded?

12 Who advised Bonnie Prince Charlie not to fight a final battle at Culloden?

13 In which city was the 1427 Parliament held at which James I ordered the imprisonment of 50 Highland chiefs?

14 When was the Scottish East India Company founded?

15 Which saint arrived in Galloway in AD 397?

ANSWERS

1. Calgacus 2. 10,000 3. 1424 4. General Wade 5. 1775 6. AD 368 7. 1739 8. 1743 9. The Scots (from Ireland) 10. 1451 11. 39 12. Lord Murray 13. Inverness 14. 1698 15. Ninian

TRIVIA

1 In which year was the wearing of tartans proscribed?

2 Which star sign would a person born on St Andrew's Day have?

3 What is the name of the ancient Kincardineshire fishing village near Muchalls which was rebuilt as a model village in the 19th-century?

4 The mansion house of which famous school stands on a site that was once known as the 'Bog of Plewlands'?

5 To which Aberdeenshire town does the following saying refer? 'Turra, Turra, faur the sorra idder'.

6 How does that saying translate?

7 A building with which secret purpose, was founded at Scalan in the Braes of Glenlivet in 1717?

8 How did the Aberdeenshire cove of St Catherine's Dub get its name?

9 In which county would you find the Castle of Fedderate?

10 Who built a miniature replica of the Temple of Theseus on his estate in the 18th-century?

11 In which county is the St Cyrus Nature Reserve?

12 Who was 'Bonnie Dundee'?

13 Whose forces did he defeat in 1689?

14 In which year was the Scottish Football Association founded?

15 With which Beatles song did Wet Wet Wet reach number one in the UK singles chart?

ANSWERS

1. 1746 2. Sagittarius 3. Stranathro 4. Gordonstoun 5. Turriff 6. 'Turriff, of course, where else, in the name of mischief, would anyone want to go?' 7. A Catholic seminary 8. Because the Spanish galleon *Santa Caterina* was wrecked there in 1594 9. Aberdeenshire 10. James Ferguson 11. Kincardineshire 12. John Graham of Claverhouse, Viscount Dundee 13. General Hugh MacKay 14. 1873 15. 'With A Little Help From My Friends'

GREAT SCOT

1 According to Scottish tradition, when is it unlucky to tell the name of infants?

2 What is, or was, 'black spauld'?

3 What was the name of the 1973 report that recommended some form of assembly for Scotland?

4 Of which novel is this the first line: 'The frowsy chamber-maid of the 'Red Lion' had just finished washing the front door steps'?

5 In which North American colony did the Scottish settlement of Stuart's Town act as an outpost against the Spanish for two years?

6 Who wrote the *Last Dying Words of Bonnie Heck*?

7 Who was Bonnie Heck?

8 What, within 5000, was the population of Edinburgh in the 1680s?

9 According to Black Isle tradition, what condition is cured by rubbing the affected area against an adulterous man?

10 How many SNP candidates were elected MPs in the October 1974 general election?

11 What was the name of the famous 'smuggling laird' who lived near Palnackie, Kirkcudbrightshire, in the late 18th century?

12 What postscript to his Latin epitaph did English King Edward I dictate on his deathbed?

13 In which year did George Malcolm Thomson publish the book *Scotland: That Distressed Area*?

14 Who wrote to Henry VII of England that 'the strength of Teviotdale once destroyed, a small power would be sufficient to keep the borders of Scotland in subjection'?

15 What, in literature, is a 'Habbie Simson'?

16 Lady Grizel Baillie is associated with the building of which Berwickshire stately home in 1725?

17 Within one percentage point, what per cent of the total Scottish electorate voted for devolution in the March 1979 referendum?

18 What did the term 'wad-setters' mean in 18th-century Scotland?

19 The political tract *Does Haughty Gaul Invasion Threat?* was written by whom?

20 Which Dundee Prohibitionist and socialist defeated Winston Churchill to become an MP in the 1922 general election?

21 Where, and to whom, did the Scots lose Fort St Andrew in 1700?

22 Which book was first edited by Sir James Murray of Denholm, Roxburghshire?

23 Edgar Atheling's sister married whom?

24 In which year was the 'Poker Club' founded in Edinburgh?

25 Article XXI of the Act of Union 1707 guaranteed the continuance of what, 'for all time coming'?

26 In which year was the first Secretary of State for Scotland appointed?

27 Which animal is considered unlucky by fishermen around Scotland?

28 Which Whig newspaper was first published in Edinburgh in 1718?

29 Which fishing station, near Wick, was established in 1787?

30 Whose illegitimate daughter was the 'Bonnie Lass of Albany'?

31 Where would you find the Myreton Motor Museum?

32 What unexpected role did Robert the Bruce's camp servants play in the victory at Bannockburn?

33 Which Highland lament was played on the carillon of St Giles, Edinburgh on May, 1 1707, when the Acts of Union came into force?

34 Whose supporters were known as the *Squadrone Volante* in the early 18th century?

35 Which famous historical figure had the title 'mormaer of Moreb'?

36 What was Andrew Bonar Law's profession before turning to politics?

37 Who wrote *Industries of Scotland*, published in 1869?

38 How did the Long Island of Lewis and Harris become noteworthy during the First World War?

39 In what year did Robert Napier and George Burns found the Cunard Line?

40 In traditional Borders weddings, what item is filled with salt and jumped over three times by the bride and bridegroom?

GREAT SCOT

41 Which Middlesbrough family discovered a method of using phosphoric ores in steel-making?

42 In a cave on which island in Campbeltown Loch did Archibald MacKinnon paint a famous Crucifixion scene in 1887?

43 Name the exact years when Holyroodhouse sheltered exiled French monarchs.

44 Which English king released William the Lion from his homage for Scotland, and under what terms?

45 Where, in Skye, did the 'Battle of the Braes' take place in the 1880s?

46 Of which novel is this the first line: 'All children, except one, grow up'?

47 What did the Act anent Peace and War, passed by the Scottish Parliament in 1703, specify?

48 Who was Governor-General of Scotland between 1807 and 1813?

49 What architectural distinction does Castle Sween, Argyll, hold?

50 The words 'ingle', 'augel' and 'aingeal' are used in various parts of Scotland as a superstitious replacement for which word?

51 Whom did Edward I of England have imprisoned in a wooden cage at the top of Berwick Castle?

52 Whose nickname was 'Bobbing John'?

53 Who was the first native-born Scot to be canonised by the Vatican?

54 Of which novel is this the first line: 'I will begin the story of my adventures with a certain morning early in the month of June, the year of grace 1751, when I took the key for the last time out of the door of my father's house'?

55 Where did 12 Scottish noblemen meet English King Edward I in 1290 to discuss their competing claims to the Scottish throne?

56 In which county would find the mouth of the River Kip?

57 On which island would you find the Little Theatre at Dervaig?

58 Which Perthshire village was the seat of the Regality Court of the Lords of Atholl?

59 At what elevation, within 9 metres or 30 feet, is the 'Rest and be thankful' stone seat in Argyll?

60 Why, traditionally, would people place knives in the wall of a house?

61 In which year was Robert the Bruce released from excommunication?

62 Whose brother was Henry, Cardinal of York, who died in 1807?

63 The ancient stone fort of Kemp Castle stands on Turin Hill, just over three miles from which town?

64 Where could you see the painting *Still Life and Table* (1947), by Ben Nicholson?

65 The Rev Lewis Balfour, grandfather of Robert Louis Stevenson, was minister of which Ayrshire parish for 23 years?

66 According to Hebridean tradition, on which day is it unlucky to kill a goat?

67 How did Scottish peasants capture Linlithgow Castle from the English in 1313?

68 Who wrote the fiddle tune 'The Miller o' Hirn'?

69 What does the 'Turk' in the Perthshire place-name Brig o' Turk mean?

70 Whose sister married King Eric II of Norway?

71 Which Kincardineshire rock is often called the 'Old Man of Muchalls'?

72 Near which Kincardineshire village is the Auquhollie standing stone, with its inscription in Ogham?

73 Whose death deprived the Old Pretender of vital continental support in the '15?

74 The Loch o' the Lowes, Perthshire, has a special hide for viewing what?

75 What is the ancient name of the district around the upper reaches of the Firth of Forth?

76 What, according to Scots tradition, should be kept in one's pocket upon seeing a New Moon?

77 What was the title of Macduff, contemporary of Macbeth?

78 What term is used to describe Edward III's devastation of Lothian in January 1356?

79 Of which novel is this the first line: 'Curdie was the son of Peter the miner'?

80 Edzell Castle, Angus, is noted for its *viridarium*. What is a *viridarium*?

ANSWERS

1 Before they are christened
2 A blood disease affecting cattle
3 The Kilbrandon Report
4 *The House with the Green Shutters*, by George Douglas Brown
5 South Carolina
6 Hamilton of Gilbertfield
7 A greyhound
8 60,000
9 Warts
10 Eleven
11 Kipp Cairns, or Cairns of Kipp
12 *Scotorum malleus*, or 'the Hammer of the Scots'
13 1937
14 The Earl of Surrey, in1523
15 A rhyme scheme (a a a b a b)
16 Mellerstain
17 32.85 per cent
18 Mortgagees
19 Robert Burns
20 Neddy Scrymgeour
21 In Panama, to the Spanish
22 The *New Oxford English Dictionary*
23 Malcolm Canmore
24 1758
25 The historic counties and burghs of Scotland, abolished in 1975
26 1926
27 The pig
28 The *Edinburgh Evening Courant*
29 Pulteneytown
30 Bonnie Prince Charlie and Clementina Walkinshaw
31 Aberlady, East Lothian
32 They appeared behind Robert's troop to watch the battle and the English thought they were replacement troops and fled
33 'Why Should I Be Sad On My Wedding Day?'
34 The 2nd Marquis of Tweeddale
35 Macbeth
36 Iron merchant
37 David Bremner
38 By suffering more casualties, in proportion to the population, than any other British region
39 1839
40 A chamber pot

41 The Gilchrists
42 Davaar Island
43 1795–1799 and 1831
44 Richard the Lion Heart, in return for a large contribution to the Third Crusade
45 Glendale
46 *Peter Pan*, by J M Barrie
47 That no successor of Queen Anne should declare a war involving Scotland without consulting the Scottish Parliament
48 Lord Minto
49 It is thought to be the earliest stone castle in Scotland
50 'Fire' (when used for a kiln)
51 The Countess of Buchan
52 The eleventh Earl of Mar
53 Saint John Ogilvie
54 *Kidnapped*, by Robert Louis Stevenson
55 Norham
56 Renfrewshire
57 Mull
58 Logierait
59 262 metres (860 feet)
60 To protect against fairies (who do not like iron)
61 1328
62 Bonnie Prince Charlie
63 Forfar
64 The Art Gallery and Regional Museum, Aberdeen
65 Sorn
66 Christmas day
67 A farmer left his haycart in the castle entrance, making it impossible to close the gate or lower the portcullis
68 Scott Skinner, the 'Strathspey King'
69 A boar
70 Robert the Bruce
71 The Auld Carl
72 Raedykes
73 Louis XIV of France
74 Nesting ospreys
75 Stone of Manau
76 A piece of silver
77 Thane of Fife
78 'Burnt Candlemas'
79 *The Princess and Curdie*, by George MacDonald
80 A walled garden

NOTES

NOTES

NOTES

NOTES

NOTES

NOTES

NOTES

NOTES

NOTES

NOTES

NOTES

NOTES

NOTES

NOTES